English for
Telecoms
and Information Technology

EXPRESS SERIES

Tom Ricca-McCarthy &
Michael Duckworth

OXFORD
UNIVERSITY PRESS

Contents

About the book

English for Telecoms and Information Technology is designed for anyone working in these sectors. The book looks at how the sectors are becoming increasingly converged, so that you can make phone calls on your PC and send emails from your mobile phone. Convergence is also occurring at an industry level, causing more and more companies to compete in the same market places. The opening unit focuses on this convergence, while the closing unit looks at the effect of technology in and on society. The remaining units each examine an area of technology in the context of a specific sector. For example, Unit 2 looks at mobility and retail, students hear about a businesswoman who needs to upgrade to a smart phone and a laptop. The shop which she visits has its own problems and gets the latest mobile EPOS terminals. Finally the same businesswoman attends a seminar to learn about the advantage of location-based services. Similarly Unit 4 looks at networking in the context of oil exploration. An oil company finds oil in a remote area and needs to set up a network to service their new office.

Each unit begins with a **Starter**, a warm-up activity that introduces the theme of the unit. The units are each divided into three cycles that are made up of a main listening or reading text and followed by comprehension, language, and communication activities. This structure allows students to acquire new language by hearing or reading it used in context and then practising it in intensive and extensive activities. Students will also encounter authentic documents that are commonly used in the industry such as Gantt charts or Reports.

Students are encouraged to interact with the material by writing comments in response to blogs and to give their opinions on the changes in technology. Realistic role-plays used with role-play cards from the **Partner Files** allow students to practise what they have learnt in authentic situations. An Output closes every unit with a demanding and authentic text and students are encouraged to take personal points of view through the accompanying **Over to you** discussions.

The **MultiROM** contains all the **Listening extracts** from the book. These can be played through the audio player on your computer, or through a conventional CD player. In order to give yourself extra listening practice, listen to it in your car. The **Interactive exercises** let you review your learning by doing **Useful phrases**, **Vocabulary**, and **Communication** exercises on your computer. This will be particularly valuable if you are using the book for self-study. There is also the **Tech Tutorials** glossary of technical language supplied as a PDF.

1 Convergence in Telecoms and IT

Work with a partner. Make a list of all the things some of the latest mobile devices can replace. Look at the screen of the device below for ideas.

CONVERGENCE IN TECHNOLOGY

1   **Read the blog post below and underline the questions it asks.**

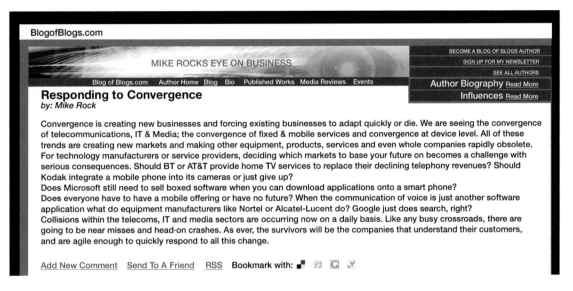

Discuss the questions with your partner.

2   **Write a comment in response to this blog post.**

3   **Complete the table below with the names of the companies that provided you with the different services in the past and in the present. Then try to predict which company might provide the services in the future.**

	Fixed phone	Mobile phone	Internet	TV
Seven years ago				
Now				
In seven years				

When you have finished, compare your answers with your partner.

TECH TUTORIAL

3G, 4G
New generations of mobile phone standards, allowing mobile network operators to offer advanced services

Ethernet
A very high bandwidth data networking technology used by companies in LANs and increasingly WANs

GSM = Global System for mobile communications
A worldwide standard for mobile phones making phones from one operator compatible with a different operator in another country

MPLS = Multi-Protocol Label Switching
A data networking protocol and service that can carry different kinds of traffic – voice, data, video etc.

Open source
Software that is made available to developers and users, licensed to encourage re-use without charge.

SaaS = Software as a Service

Wi-Fi
A technology providing wireless transmission of data over a short range (for example, in a house or office)

Wi-Max
A technology providing wireless transmission of high speed data over a large area (for example, a city)

4   **Read the magazine article about trends in Telecoms and IT. Match the industry leader to their area of expertise.**

1   Peter Wilson   a software
2   Jenny Lane   b telecoms
3   Sanjay Ravi   c hardware

STATE OF PLAY

To celebrate our 10th anniversary, we invited industry leaders to share their thoughts about the changing world of Telecoms and IT. To find out what they think, read on …

Peter Wilson

The world is now plugged in, and countries are connected up using a mixture of terrestrial networks, undersea cables, satellite and micro-wave communications, Wi-Max and Wi-Fi, GSM and 3G. The move from packet-based services to the internet protocol means everyone expects to communicate voice, data and video from anywhere to anywhere, globally. The availability of wide area data services such as MPLS and Ethernet have spread all over the world, allowing companies to manage and communicate with their operations wherever they may be.

A reason for this has been the fall in bandwidth costs, and broadband is getting cheaper and cheaper. Services can now deliver tens or even hundreds of megabits of bandwidth into individual homes for much less money than a 64Kb line that a whole factory might have used to run its operation only a few years ago.

Jenny Lane

In 1965 Gordon Moore stated that the number of transistors on a chip would double about every two years. And that has more or less remained true since then. As we write, a single chip can hold about 1 billion transistors each making 3 billion binary calculations per second.

There has been a huge increase in the volume of data and data storage capacity required for this; secondly, there has been a significant decrease in the size and power consumption of hardware and finally manufacturing costs are falling significantly. The result is that there are more and more powerful computers in our lives, and even handheld devices can store gigabytes of data holding thousands of MP3 music files or hundreds of films.

Sanjay Ravi

The internet is changing the way we access, buy and use applications. We go online and download the software we want onto our computer, like any other digital product. Increasingly we don't even have the software on our hardware, but visit an internet site and use that application as a service. The use of this Software as a Service (SaaS) model means that we may not need such powerful computers in the future.

We have seen the impact of off-shoring and the rise of India as the world centre of software development and application management. We are also seeing some of the smartest applications and services coming out of people's bedrooms; more and more experts are producing Open source software, which is becoming more and more popular, creating a real threat to the big corporations.

5   Read the text again. Say if the following statements are TRUE (T) or FALSE (F) according to the text.

According to Peter Wilson:

1   most countries are connected up with undersea cables. ☐
2   many countries have unreliable mobile phone networks. ☐
3   recently bandwidth costs have risen dramatically. ☐

According to Jenny Lane:

4   Moore's predictions have been fairly accurate. ☐
5   a typical chip can now hold 3 billion transistors. ☐
6   both data storage capacity and power consumption have gone up. ☐

According to Sanjay Ravi:

7   fewer people are going to computer stores to buy software. ☐
8   SaaS will require ordinary users to have more powerful computers. ☐
9   software development needs the support of a big corporation to succeed. ☐

6   Match the words on the left with the words on the right to make pairs of words that often go together. The word on the left must go with all three words in the set. See the example.

1   access   a   chip, wafer, valley
2   download   b   an application, a network, an account
3   go   c   online, offline, on holiday
4   mobile   d   phone, telephony, broadband
5   silicon   e   a file, an image, a demo version

7   Complete the sentences using pairs of words from exercise 6. Make any changes that are necessary.

1   Everyone has _____, so payphones are becoming redundant.
2   Many internet entrepreneurs from _____ in California are now turning their attention to alternative forms of energy.
3   Before you buy the program, you can _____ just to see how you like it.
4   With a mobile broadband connection, you can _____ any time and anywhere.
5   Internet banking allows users to _____ and check their balances.
6   How many transistors can you fit onto a _____?

TALKING ABOUT CHANGE

We can use the present continuous to talk about change.
*Manufacturing costs **are falling** significantly*
*More and more experts **are producing** Open source software.*

We often use one or more comparative adjectives to talk about change.
*Broadband is getting **cheaper and cheaper**.*
*Open source software is becoming **more and more popular**.*

8 **Complete the sentences with the words in brackets, making any changes that are necessary.**

1   Digital radio sets _____*are becoming*_____ (become) less and less popular.
2   More and more people _____ (listen) to radio over the internet.
3   Laptops are getting _____ (cheap).
4   Handheld devices are becoming _____ (sophisticated).
5   Battery life _____ (get) _____ (long)
6   In some areas, VoIP _____ (take over) from PSTN.
7   Mobile broadband speeds _____ (increase) dramatically.

CONVERGENCE IN BUSINESS

9 **New words are continually being created in Telecoms and IT. Often these words are made up of two parts. Match the openings in Column A with the correct endings in Column B. See the example.**

A	B	New words
UP-	-space, -crime	
DOWN-	-load, -grade, -date	upload, upgrade, update
E-	-time, -load	
TELE-	-book, -mail, -commerce	
CYBER-	-working, -conferencing, -coms	

Now match the openings in Column A with the endings in Column B

A	B	New words
hard- , ad-, spy-	-BAND	
wave-, broad-, narrow-	-BYTE	
broad-, pod-, news-	-CAST	
smart-, cell-, i-, head-	-WARE	
kilo-, mega-, giga-	-PHONE	

Can you think of any other words with these openings and endings?

10 **Complete the sentences using a suitable word from exercise 9.**

1 _____ is increasing, so more and more people have an office at home and aren't commuting to an office.

2 The police are recruiting IT experts to deal with the alarming increase in _____.

3 Each memory module contains a _____ of RAM, or 1024 megabytes, to be precise.

4 Our servers are very reliable, so we have hardly any _____.

5 This anti-virus program scans your PC for _____ that threatens your security.

6 Did you buy a full version of the OS or just an _____?

AUDIO
2–6

11 **Five people are talking about their work. Listen to the extracts. Write down any of the new words from exercise 9 that include the words in capitals. See the example.**

Speaker 1   (-PHONE)   _*Cellphone*_   (UP-)   _____

Speaker 2   (-CAST)   _____   (DOWN-)   _____

Speaker 3   (-WARE)   _____   (TELE-)   _____

Speaker 4   (UP-)   _____   (-BYTE)   _____

Speaker 5   (TELE-)   _____   (-BAND)   _____

12 **Listen again. Tick (✔) the boxes to show what each speaker manufactures or provides. You may tick more than one box for each speaker.**

Which speaker:	1	2	3	4	5
manufactures hardware?	☐	☐	☐	☐	☐
manufactures traditional software?	☐	☐	☐	☐	☐
provides a search engine?	☐	☐	☐	☐	☐
provides SaaS (software as a service)?	☐	☐	☐	☐	☐
enables voice telephony?	☐	☐	☐	☐	☐
provides TV?	☐	☐	☐	☐	☐

13 **Discuss these questions with a partner.**

1 Where do you think there is the most competition between the speakers?

2 Where do you think there is the least competition?

3 In your line of business, what are your biggest opportunities?

4 In your line of business, what are the biggest threats to your company?

14 **Match a word from column A with a word from column B to make pairs that were used in the listening. Listen again if necessary.**

A	B
broadband	technology
data	provider
digital	calls
disruptive	pipe
internet	engine
search	access
service	camera
voice	centre

15 **Complete the sentences with word pairs from exercise 14.**

1   A _____ is an organization that gives its customers facilities such as internet access or mobile telephony.

2   Traditionally, telecoms companies made most of their profits from _____, but they have had to diversify into other areas.

3   A _____ is a high speed communications channel using a wire or optical cable.

4   A _____ is a facility where a company's data and applications can be stored securely.

5   A _____ is a new invention or process that provides a new product or service in an unexpected way.

6   With a 3G-enabled phone, you can have high speed _____ 24/7 wherever you go.

7   Google rapidly became the most widely used _____ in the 1990s.

8   The quality of a _____ depends on the number of pixels and the lens.

A CONVERGED FUTURE

AUDIO
7

16 **Listen to Ian Pearson, a futurologist, talking about the development of technologies and the impact these could have on business and society. The coloured lines on the diagram on page 11 represent different areas Ian talks about. Label the lines with the areas below.**

1   Telecoms

2   Society

3   Business

4   Software and hardware

17 **Listen again and match the numbered boxes on the diagram on page 11 with the innovations below.**

a   contact lens display screens

b   RFID replaces barcodes

c   biometric scanners replace ID cards

d   free voice calls

e   VR escapism a growing social problem

f   thought recognition

g   desktop computers that can compute as fast as the human brain

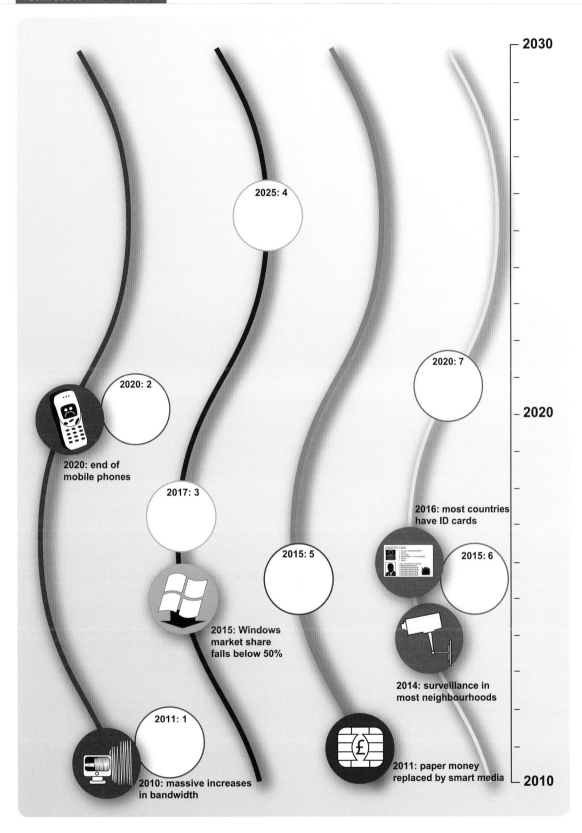

2030

2025: 4

2020: 2

2020: 7

2020

2020: end of
mobile phones

2017: 3

2016: most countries
have ID cards

2015: 5

2015: 6

2015: Windows
market share
falls below 50%

2014: surveillance in
most neighbourhoods

2011: 1

2011: paper money
replaced by smart media

2010: massive increases
in bandwidth

2010

18 **Discuss these questions or write down short answers.**

1   Have any of these predictions already come true?
2   Are there any predictions that will come true sooner than the extract suggests?
3   Are there any of these predictions that you think will not come true?
4   What other predictions would you make about the future of hardware, software, telecoms, or IT?

DEGREES OF PROBABILITY IN THE FUTURE

We can use different expressions to talk about how sure we are that something will happen in the future.

100%	will definitely	*is/are sure to, is/are bound to, is/are certain to*
75 %	will probably	*is/are likely to, there's a good chance that*
50 %	will possibly	*may, might, could*
25%	probably won't	*is/are unlikely to*
0%	definitely won't	*there's no chance that*

---

19 **Re-write these sentences using the word in brackets. See the example.**

A lot of companies are likely to go out of business. (probably)
A lot of companies will probably go out of business.

1   Windows is unlikely to remain the dominant force in software. (probably)

_____

2   People could stop using cash by around 2015. (may)

_____

3   The mouse will definitely disappear in the next few years. (bound)

_____

4   There's a very good chance that mobile phones will be replaced with something different. (probably)

_____

5   There is no chance that the rate of change will slow down. (definitely)

_____

20 **Work with a partner. You each have some predictions about two more areas of technology. Use the expressions from the language box above to show how sure you are about your predictions. Mark the predictions onto the black timeline on page 11.**

 Partner A   File 1, p. 75
Partner B   File 1, p. 77

Read the newsfeeds about Telecoms and IT and answer the questions below.

Nokia laptops?

In another example of convergence, Nokia is considering a move into the PC market. Unlike netbook and notebook specialists Acer, who unveiled a new smart phone at the Mobile World Congress, Nokia is going in the other direction.

Lower and lower

India has announced plans to produce an educational laptop, the 'Sakshat', which will allow millions of schoolchildren to have access to the internet. The machine will sell for just $20, but will come with wireless connectivity and 2GB of RAM.

Clouds ahead

In a new move into the world of cloud computing, Google has announced plans for the Google drive or Gdrive. Instead of storing information on PCs or laptops, users will be able to store data and applications on Google servers and access them over the internet.

Is Skype now the biggest Telecoms company in the world?

According to TeleGeography, Skype handled 33 billion cross border minutes in 2008, up 41%, against an industry increase of just 12%. Skype now accounts for 8% of the international voice. Other VoIP providers make up a further 23% of the international market.

One billion downloads in nine months

Apple announced that 13-year-old Conor Mulcahey downloaded the billionth app from the iTunes store. Apps use the technology of the iPhone like the Multi-Touch interface, the accelerometer, GPS, real-time 3D graphics, and 3D positional audio. Most other operators and manufacturers are trying to enter this popular market.

Adobe Flash on TV

Adobe has secured a deal to put Flash software onto the chips most commonly used inside TV sets and set top boxes. The move should facilitate the creation of web-based content on TV screens. The move further develops the increasing convergence of TV and PC/internet in the home with users likely to use their TVs for internet searches and increasing consumption of online media content.

Alcatel-Lucent posts eighth loss in a row

Alcatel-Lucent, the world's third largest telecom equipment manufacturer, reported its eighth straight quarterly loss. The €3.89bn loss was said to reflect the drastic deterioration of the global outlook and the change in strategy.

According to the newsfeeds:

1 Where are Nokia and Acer already competing?
2 How much will the Sakshat cost?
3 How will users access the Gdrive?
4 What is the total VoIP market share for international voice?
5 How long has it taken Apple to generate one billion downloads?
6 For how many months in a row has Alcatel-Lucent made a loss?

OVER TO YOU

- Do you know of any developments to the stories in the news feeds?
- What are the latest examples of technology companies converging that you have noticed?
- What sorts of companies do you think will be the big winners and losers in a converged future?

2 Mobility

How mobile are you? Complete the questionnaire and then compare with a partner.

When you are on the move, how often do you:	Never	Sometimes	Often
speak to family?			
speak to work colleagues?			
speak to customers?			
buy something?			
check your bank account?			
listen to music?			
send emails?			
write presentations?			
build spreadsheets?			
access an information database?			
download and use a new application?			
use Location-Based Services?			

Discuss what device you use for these activities.

MOBILE DEVICES

AUDIO
8

1 **Listen to the conversation between Antonia Gomez, who runs a small food export company, and Kate, a sales assistant in a branch of TopTech, a chain of technology shops. She is explaining what communications technology she needs and Kate is giving her advice.**

Match the sentence halves to complete what Antonia says she needs to do.

1	it's not very convenient	a	charging my phone in a customer's office
2	it's a bit embarrassing	b	be able to do all these things on the move
3	I want	c	emails all the time
4	I send and receive	d	be able to read the attachments
5	I need to	e	the basic functionality of my current phone
6	I'd like to	f	only being able to access all my information when I'm in the office

TECH TUTORIAL

Bluetooth
A technology that allows short-range, wireless connection between devices
LBS = Location-Based Services
Information, products, or services provided to you based on the location of your device (using GPS or the mobile network)
GPRS = General Packet Radio Service
Provides packet-based connections on mobile networks
GPS = Global Positioning System
Allows receiver to identify its position anywhere on earth

2 **Listen again and complete the two tables of features for the SuperMob 360 and the Silver Lite A2. Tick (✓) the features that Kate mentions.**

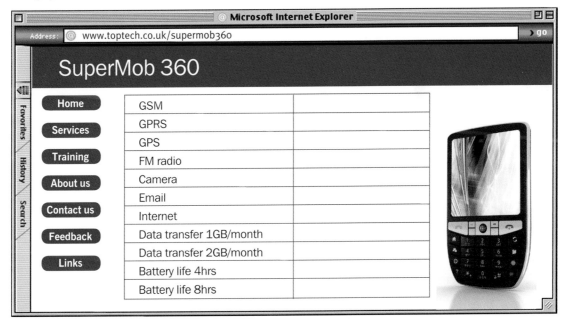

SuperMob 360 — www.toptech.co.uk/supermob360

GSM	
GPRS	
GPS	
FM radio	
Camera	
Email	
Internet	
Data transfer 1GB/month	
Data transfer 2GB/month	
Battery life 4hrs	
Battery life 8hrs	

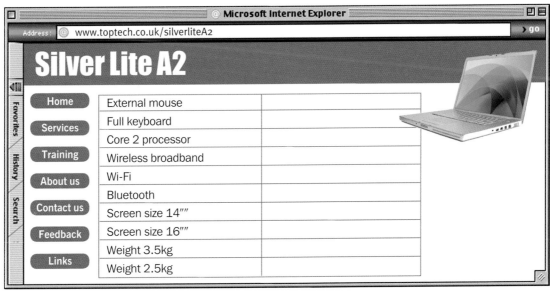

Silver Lite A2 — www.toptech.co.uk/silverliteA2

External mouse	
Full keyboard	
Core 2 processor	
Wireless broadband	
Wi-Fi	
Bluetooth	
Screen size 14""	
Screen size 16""	
Weight 3.5kg	
Weight 2.5kg	

3 Work with a partner. One of you is a sales assistant and the other is a customer. Look at the language box below and role play the situation.

PARTNER FILES → Partner A File 2, p. 75
Partner B File 2, p. 77

EXPRESSING NEEDS AND RECOMMENDING

Needs	Recommending
I want...	What I'd recommend is ...
I need to...	I'd go for ...
I'd like to...	It would be worth getting ...
It's not very convenient only...	You should get ...
It's important for me to...	You could try ...

4 Imagine you are Antonia Gomez. You want to buy the SuperMob 360 but it isn't in stock and the sales assistant needs to go to the warehouse to check she has the Silver Lite A2. What would you do?

1 Walk out of the shop and buy the same products online (they will probably be cheaper).
2 Wait to see if they have the laptop.
3 Tell the sales assistant to call you once she has the products you want.

AUDIO

9

MOBILE TECHNOLOGY IN RETAIL

5 Antonia Gomez walked out of the shop and bought the products online. This is not the first customer TopTech has lost due to similar problems. Listen to the message Bob Murray, the store manager, left Malcolm Frith, TopTech's IT Director. Complete the table below with his complaints.

Supply chain	Warehousing	Tills	Customer service
Can't see what's going out and what's coming in			

6 Complete the email that Malcolm sent Bob with the words in the box.

terminals • schedules • chain • trends • converged • continuous • stock • renewal

Dear Bob

I'm sorry to hear about the business issues you are experiencing due to our IT infrastructure. There has been a lot of activity in the background and we are on the verge of a major IT _____[1] programme that will address your concerns. Please read the attachment to this email which details what the new system will do.

Basically the new system will give you complete supply _____[2] visibility, guaranteed _____[3] replenishment of stock, electronic tagging, electronic point-of-sale _____[4], and _____[5] fixed-to-mobile phones.

As well as the systems outlined in the attachment we will all receive better management of information from the new systems. Store Managers will receive a number of automatic reports at 0900 every day, detailing the previous day's trading, _____[6] levels, delivery _____[7], and buying _____[8].

I hope this helps address some of your concerns. Please feel free to contact me to discuss the rollout schedule for your particular store.

Regards, Malcolm

7 Read the attachment.

Supply Chain

Single, fully integrated Supply Chain Management solution to be implemented. This will:

- give visibility across the supply chain from store/warehouse to distribution centre.
- give information on what suppliers are manufacturing and when products will be available.
- host new servers and applications at TopTech data centre with rollout of new IP network to all stores & suppliers.
- display stock levels in real time so when an item is purchased a replacement order is automatically placed with suppliers to replenish stock.
- automatically schedule a delivery when stocks reduce to a certain point, to ensure new stock arrives at store before inventory depletes.

Warehousing

RFID solution to be implemented. This will:

- tag all goods to make them identifiable at all times throughout supply chain.
- allow sensors in loading bay and warehouse to monitor deliveries, locate items in warehouse, and track purchases.
- reduce shrinkage through increased monitoring.

Tills

Legacy equipment to be replaced with EPOS touch screen terminals. These:

- can be positioned anywhere in store and connect via wireless LAN.
- have software to allow staff to check stock levels and give customers up-to-date information allowing staff to suggest alternative products if others not in stock.
- include two wireless Waiter Pads per store which staff can use as mobile tills as they attend customers anywhere in store.
- use latest chip and pin technology for increased security.
- will be integrated into supply chain and data centre with new pricing and campaign information uploaded daily.

Customer Service

- single number for customers to call with calls handled at a centralized call centre to keep store staff free to deal with customers.
- all staff to be issued with a cordless phone to receive any calls that do have to come through to the shop floor. These phones are converged fixed-to-mobile phones which operate as telephone extensions in store but operate off-site as mobile phones without call interruption.

8 Find words in the attachment that mean:

1	are making	5	runs out
2	installing new systems	6	loss of stock
3	show	7	old and out of date
4	bought	8	not in the company's buildings

TECH TUTORIAL

EPOS = Electronic Point Of Sale
A networked and programmable electronic till

RFID = Radio Frequency IDentification
A system of tags and readers that communicate information via radio frequency

LAN = Local Area Network
A computer network covering a local area, such as a home or an office

9 Complete the email that Bob sent to his staff about the new systems. Use your notes from exercise 5 and the details in Malcolm's email attachment to explain, in simple terms, what the new system will mean for the staff.

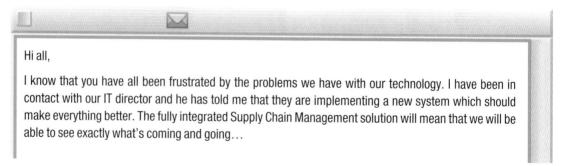

Hi all,

I know that you have all been frustrated by the problems we have with our technology. I have been in contact with our IT director and he has told me that they are implementing a new system which should make everything better. The fully integrated Supply Chain Management solution will mean that we will be able to see exactly what's coming and going…

10 Use the clues to complete this puzzle and find the hidden word related to stock planning.

1 An acronym for a system of tagging products
2 A document that accompanies an email
3 A *Blackberry* is a type of *hand-held* …
4 An acronym for a type of electronic till
5 Laptops can be *Wi-fi-*…
6 A technology that allows short-range, wireless technology
7 To put something on to a system such as the internet
8 A place to store goods
9 The process of getting goods from manufacturers to shops (two words: 6, 5)

LOCATION-BASED SERVICES

11 Match the words with the definitions.

1	Mapping	a	finding the best route from one point to another.
2	Tracking	b	following the progress of a moving vehicle or person
3	Navigation	c	creating an image or diagram of an area

When do you or your company use a *mobile* device to help with each of these?

Can you think of any uses that other organizations (e.g. police, insurance companies) have for these technologies?

AUDIO

10

12 Antonia Gomez is thinking of opening a retail outlet for her food products and is interested in understanding how to apply location-based services to attract customers to her outlet. She attends a seminar on the subject at a retail and mobility conference to find out more.

Listen to the seminar and match the words with the meanings.

1	geomarketing	a	gives personal information to (a service)
2	subscribes to (a service)	b	time taken to travel from a satellite and back
3	inputs to (a service)	c	advertising to people depending on where they are
4	mash up	d	pays a regular amount for (a service)
5	transit time	e	an electronic signal sent by a satellite to a mobile device
6	timing signal	f	combine different types of information from different sources

13 Listen to the extract again. Say if the following statements are TRUE (T) or FALSE (F).

1 Most smart phones can use GPS technology. ☐
2 Antonia could alert people with mobiles that they are near her shop. ☐
3 Geomarketing can give consumers useful local information. ☐
4 Antonia is planning to open a chain of pizza restaurants. ☐
5 A user's location can be calculated to the nearest 60 metres. ☐
6 Antonia thinks the system would be suitable for her business. ☐

14 In your opinion, what are:

1 the two biggest advantages to a business of using location-based services?
2 the two biggest advantages to a consumer of using location-based services?
3 the two biggest disadvantages to a business of using location-based services?
4 the two biggest disadvantages to a consumer of using location-based services?

Compare your opinions with a partner.

OUTPUT

Read the article and answer the questions.

Retail Week

Latest retail news, jobs, analysis and market data

Cash, card or mobile phone?
Right now, retailers need to get to grips with the dawn of contactless payment

In the past week there has been a raft of announcements and news on alternative payment methods. Technologists everywhere are still convinced that they can come up with something better than cash for smaller transactions.

The alternative method that retailers must consider in the immediate future is contactless payment. A few stores in London have gone live with the Barclaycard Business contactless payment system already, more than 1,000 other sites have signed up to use it, and 3,000 consumers have registered their interest in the system's OnePulse contactless card.

A recent YouGov survey commissioned by an ATM operator highlighted that consumers have fraud concerns about contactless payment. Yet similar surveys of online shopping also tend to highlight significant fraud fears, while the number of people and volume of their online transactions continues to grow.

In the longer term, the techies are still betting on the mobile phone becoming the new wallet. PayPal has gone live with a mobile payment system already. Others are still very much a work in progress; such as the mobile payment system dubbed GPay that it has emerged Google has filed a patent for.

Another, PayForIt, is a mobile payment scheme for transactions under £10 that all five major mobile network operators have signed up to. At present, it is only really being used to pay for mobile phone content. However, the plan is to expand this so consumers can make payments to online retailers when they access their sites via mobile phone.

If this seems far-fetched, just take a look at some of the retailers that have registered for .mobi internet domains – a type of web site address that highlights the fact that the site has been optimised for viewing on a mobile device.

It is good practice to buy any domain that may pertain to your brand. However, it is interesting to note that innovative retailers such as Amazon and Tesco have already secured domains that will allow them to launch mobile-optimised sites, should they wish.

Say if these statements are TRUE (T) or FALSE (F).

1 The Barclaycard Business contactless payment system is already being used in London. ☐

2 Contactless payment systems carry a greater fraud risk than online shopping. ☐

3 It seems likely that mobiles will be increasingly used for making payments. ☐

4 Major retailers are worried about the competition from mobile-optimised sites. ☐

OVER TO YOU

- Do you know of any other systems of contactless payment?
- Do you think we will ever stop using cash? If so, when?
- Do you think that contactless payment and other electronic forms of payments are more open to fraud than traditional forms of payment?
- Do you know of any retailers that have registered for .mobi internet domains?

3 Software

Think about your answers to this quiz.

Your favourite and least favourite piece of software.

I love _____ because _____
I hate _____ because _____

A piece of software you use regularly and what its main advantages and disadvantages are.

_____ is great because _____
_____ is not so great because _____

The best cheap / freeware application you have downloaded from the internet.

I love _____ because _____

Now discuss your answers with a partner.

THE SOFTWARE DEVELOPMENT PROCESS

1   Complete the diagram with information about your company's IT.

User	e.g. different departments: Finance, HR, etc.	1 _____ 2 _____ 3 _____
Application	e.g. Word, Sage	1 _____ 2 _____ 3 _____
Operating System	e.g. Windows, Linux	1 _____
Hardware	e.g. mainframe	1 _____ 2 _____ 3 _____

What problems might your company have if it took over another company that used different operating systems and applications?

2 Cleverbox is a manufacturer of a new type of IP router that is bought by telecoms network operators. It has grown rapidly, both organically and through acquisition. This rapid growth is now causing business problems with integration. The Cleverbox IT Director, Jane Simmons, sent an email to Elizabeth Hardy, from software development company Talking Software Ltd, outlining their problems.

Complete Jane's email with the expressions below.

applications • customized • data format • helpdesk • operating system • releases • software licences • upgrade

Cleverbox uses a single operating system across its departments, but many of our departments have _____ [1] their applications and processes, which means that there are _____ _____ [2] and integration problems in the company. On top of this, some departments have been slow to _____ [3], which means that different departments have different software _____ [4]. Things are getting very expensive because all of the _____ _____ [5] we have to buy. Maintaining all of this and providing _____ [6] services for our customers also costs us a lot of money.

To make things even more complicated, our latest acquisition, Smart Route, uses a completely different _____ _____ [7], which means that none of their _____ [8] will work with Cleverbox.

3 You are going to hear Elizabeth giving Jane a short sales presentation about Talking Software. Before you listen, check that you know the meanings of these words. Match the words 1–12 with the definitions a–l.

1	bespoke	a	small and medium-sized enterprises
2	bugs	b	specially produced for someone
3	cutover	c	detailed description of what is required
4	modular	d	work finished or completed
5	off the shelf	e	strong, reliable
6	output	f	standard and commercially available (package)
7	robust	g	in separate, independent sections
8	rollout	h	errors in a program
9	sign off	i	gradual implementation
10	SME	j	final move to a new system
11	specification	k	finish and leave
12	steady state	l	working properly and reliably

AUDIO

11

4 Listen to Elizabeth's presentation and complete the three slides detailing Talking Software's areas of expertise.

Business Processes

Team

_____ [1] Consultants

Tasks

_____ [2] business processes and provide a

_____ [3] or Software Requirements Analysis.

Software Development

Team

20 _____ [4], programmers and coders

Tasks

Design _____ [5] and code and compile software

Test for _____ [6]

_____ [7] existing software products

Application Implementation

Ten people led by a _____ [8]

Tasks

Install _____ [9] software

Install customized products

Install _____ [10] packages

---

5 Discuss these questions with a partner.

1 What problems have you personally had with software packages?
2 What problems has your company or organization had with software applications?
3 What problems have you seen other people or other organizations have with their software?
4 How were these problems fixed in each scenario?

6 After analysing the two businesses, Talking Software produced a report for Cleverbox. Read the Executive Summary below and match sentences 1–6 with sections i)–iv)c of the summary.

1   The accounts packages are not being used effectively.

2   Information needs to be stored in one location and this will save money.

3   The software needs standardizing and updating regularly, and this will save money.

4   The personnel departments of the two companies operate differently.

5   One of the bespoke applications is not particularly useful and cannot be used by the other company.

6   The two companies need to use a single operating system.

Cleverbox Software: Problems & Options

Executive Summary

Talking Software carried out an analysis on the IT estates of the two businesses and the high level summary is as follows:

Problems: Talking Software has noted that:

i)   The IT Infrastructure of the two businesses requires consolidation into a single data centre and database. There is an opportunity to reduce cost through server consolidation. Communications infrastructure is compatible (MPLS based) but will require some capacity increases on certain links to ensure the end users' experience of using the applications is acceptable.

ii) Server Operating Systems are incompatible being Windows and Linux. Desktop Operating Systems are also a problem because Windows and Mac OS are used.

iii) Software Licences: all departments have been purchasing their own licences and there are lots of agreements with lots of vendors and no volume discounts. There are no coordinated upgrades leaving some users and departments without the software functionality they need. This is all leading to high numbers of calls to the IT Helpdesk and significant training costs.

iv) At a departmental level there are the following issues:

a)   Human Resources: Cleverbox uses HR Pro as its HR application in real time, whilst Smart Route runs their HR activities using Microsoft Excel updated monthly.

b)   Finance: Cleverbox Finance is struggling to integrate with your own HR, Sales and Procurement applications due to different data formats and scheduling. This is leading to delays in Payroll for your own staff, late billing to your clients and late invoice payments to suppliers. Smart Route uses the Sage Release 2.0 which you will not be able to integrate to.

c)   Manufacturing: Cleverbox uses a self developed application that integrates well within the business but will be completely incompatible with Smart Route. Although it is integrated, the functionality is limited and it provides very little management information.

Options: Given the observations above we believe the options for Cleverbox management are to:

1   Invest in Smart Route to change their operating system and replace their applications to mirror Cleverbox. A second stage would then consolidate the information of both businesses into a single database. This solution will support your business for the next three years. The cost of Option 1 will be one year's profit and it will take two years to execute.

2   Scrap all the legacy software in both businesses and invest in an off-the-shelf ERP (Enterprise Resource Planning) system. This will provide a common database and synchronized data across the combined business. Modular software applications for each department allow every department to store and retrieve standardized data in real-time. This option is future proof. Option 2 will cost two years of profit and take one year to implement and will support your business for seven years.

7 **Read sections i) to iv) again. Find words or phrases that mean:**

1 joining together into one
2 able to function well together
3 improvements in size or power
4 unable to function well together
5 sellers

6 price reductions for buying in bulk
7 properly organized
8 usefulness
9 problems
10 combine to work together

8 **Use some of the words from exercise 7 to complete sentences 1–5.**

1 The trial version only has limited _____ – if you want to use all the features, you have to buy the full version.
2 We had some serious _____ with our IT infrastructure, so we called in some consultants.
3 If the printer isn't _____ with your operating system, it won't work.
4 After a series of _____, our broadband speed has now risen to 24Mbs
5 The rollout of the new software was very well _____, and everything went smoothly.
6 If all our departments buy new software licences at the same time, we'll get good _____.

9 **Look at the two options in the summary. Put these notes on each option into the correct columns.**

will last for seven years
can be done in two stages
only requires one company to change its software
will last for three years

can be implemented in a year
can be implemented over two years
will cost two years' profit
will only cost half of the other option

Option 1: features and advantages

_____
_____
_____
_____
_____

Option 2: features and advantages

_____
_____
_____

Can you add any other features or advantages to the list?

FUTURE CONSEQUENCES

We often use the first conditional to talk about the future consequences of present actions.
*If they choose option 1, it **will** cost two years' profit.*

We can also use this structure to talk about future ability and obligations.
Future ability: ***will be able to, won't be able to***
*If Smart Route changes its OS, both businesses **will be able to** use a single database.*

Future obligation: ***will have to, won't have to***
*If they choose option 2, they **will have to** pay more up front.*

---

10 **The recommendation section at the end of the Executive Summary is missing. Look at all the information in the text and discuss with a partner which option you would recommend.**

Now write a short paragraph summarizing your recommendation.

PROJECT MANAGEMENT

Cleverbox ERP Rollout Project Plan	Lead	January	February	March	April	May	June	July	August	September	October
Commercials & Governance	Elizabeth										
Negotiate & Sign Contract		5th									
Identify Stakeholders		12th									
Project Kickoff		21st									
Project Handover											5.
IT Infrastructure	Jane										
MPLS Bandwidth Increase			by 17th								
Datacentre Ready			1.								
All Departments	Pedro										
Identifying Data to be Migrated		31st									
Construct Data Template in Software			by 28th								
Configuration				2.							
Customization				22nd							
Finance	Mustafa										
Data Freeze					1st						
Migration					3.						
Test						15th					
Cutover							22nd				
Human Resources	Chuck										
Data Freeze					4.						
Migration						9th					
Test							14th				
Cutover								25th			
Procurement	Sandra										
Data Freeze							2nd				
Migration							10th				
Test								17th			
Cutover								23rd			
Manufacturing	Xu										
Data Freeze								4th			
Migration								11th			
Test								18th			
Cutover									24th		

11 Elizabeth from Talking Software is having a conference call to discuss the rollout of the new ERP software for Cleverbox. Look at the chart and answer the questions.

1 When will the project kick off?
2 Who is responsible for the Finance department?
3 What department does Chuck lead?
4 Who is in charge of upgrading the MPLS?
5 When will the data freeze start for the Finance department?
6 Which department will be migrating data on May 9th?
7 When will HR start testing?
8 When will Manufacturing cutover?

AUDIO

12

12 Listen to the extract and complete the missing dates 1–5 on the chart.

13 **Listen to the extract again. Say if the following statements are TRUE (T) or FALSE (F).**

1 Elizabeth is expecting some delays and missed deadlines. ☐
2 Elizabeth explains the workstreams involved in preparing the data templates. ☐
3 The four departments will all follow a similar procedure for the ERP rollout. ☐
4 Mustafa is unsure when the data migration will begin. ☐
5 HR cannot employ anyone new after May 3rd. ☐
6 Manufacturing will be very busy during the testing period. ☐

14 **Match the words 1–8 with the definitions a–h.**

1 bottleneck   a delay
2 within scope/out of scope   b leave unchanged
3 slippage   c blockage
4 rollout   d final date for completing (a project)
5 stick to (a date)   e move (data) from one system to another
6 dirty data   f implement and start using (new software)
7 deadline   g information with mistakes (e.g. spelling mistakes)
8 migrate   h suitable/unsuitable for inclusion

15 **Complete this extract from an email using some of the words above.**

> I'm sorry to have to tell you that there has been some _____ [1] in the project and we won't
> be able to _____ [2] our original _____ [3] on July 30th for completing the
> _____ [4] of the new software.
> Pedro's absence for three weeks caused a bit of a _____ [5], and there were more
> delays when we realised that there was still some _____ [6] in the database that needed
> cleaning up.
> Still, I am confident that we can complete the project by the end of next month.

TIME PERIODS

Prepositions and time words
Look at the prepositions we normally use with these time expressions.

at	6.15	**on**	Monday
	the end of the month		the 15th
	the weekend		August 11th

in	August	**no preposition**	yesterday
	2007		last week
	the 1990s		next week
			tomorrow

by* and *until
by means not later than.
I need that report by Wednesday.
(Monday, Tuesday or Wednesday will be OK.
Thursday will be too late.)

until means from time A (often now) to time B
*We will be working with you until the project is
completed.*
(We will be working here from now up to the
end of the project.)

16 Complete the sentences with *by, until, in, on, at,* or - (no preposition).

1 Would you mind waiting _____ Mrs Langton gets back?
2 By the way, could I remind everyone that our next meeting will be _____ Tuesday 18th _____ 11.10.
3 I had a few problems connecting to the internet _____ I installed Wi-Fi.
4 Could you give this invoice to Helen? I think she's coming in _____ tomorrow.
5 My father worked for NCR until he retired _____ 1990.
6 We can't use the new system _____ it has been fully tested.
7 I need that report _____ 6.30 tomorrow at the latest.
8 What did you do _____ the weekend? Did you go to London?

17 Listen to Pedro's description of the process. Complete the extracts with the missing words.

1 _____ _____ _____, we need to identify all the data that you each have to migrate ...
2 _____ each department will then construct a data template ...
3 ... this needs to be done _____ the end of next month.
4 _____ _____ , the database will be configured ...
5 _____, any customization of your templates or processes must be completed ...

18 Read the situations below and choose one. Think about five steps for each situation. Use some of the sequencing words above to explain your situation briefly to a partner or write a short paragraph putting the steps in sequence.

1 A non-expert wants to format the hard drive on his PC and re-load the operating system, but doesn't want to lose any important files or emails. Explain the steps in this procedure.
2 A company is moving to new premises in the same city. Explain what steps they need to take to make sure that their IT system can move with the minimum amount of disruption.
3 The Finance Department of a small company has decided to start using a new accounts package. Explain what steps it needs to take to use the software effectively.

19 Work with a partner to complete the work streams in a software rollout programme.

PARTNER FILES   Partner A File 3, p.75
                Partner B File 3, p.77

OUTPUT

Read the article about cloud computing and answer the questions below.

Who is in the cloud?

The "cloud" and cloud-computing are among the buzz words of the year. The big players are moving into this area in a big way. Google will already run your email and host your documents, and its App Engine lets users run custom applications. Amazon has a service that allows users to set up virtual servers on the internet, and Microsoft is joining the party with Windows Azure.

At the same time, the concept of cloud computing is far from new, and one company that has been in the business since 1999 (an age in internet terms) is salesforce.com. The business lets customers manage their sales data, leads and other information on the internet using salesforce.com's online applications, and with over $1 bn in annual revenue, it is clearly a model that works. Marc Benioff, the company's 44-year-old chief executive and co-founder is convinced that cloud computing is the way ahead. 'This is the future,' he says. 'If it isn't, I don't know what is. We're in it. You're going to see this model dominate our industry.'

Benioff sees the service cloud as the alternative to call centres and telephone helplines. He believes that when customers have a problem with a product or service they no longer call a helpline, they go to Google. Companies like Orange are already using the service cloud, where they can set up their own web portal with links to customer services and other applications.

But are there any dangers to this the brave new world? When Gmail was hit by an outage in February, Twitter was alive with cries about the risks of moving mission-critical data and applications outside your own IT department's control, even though the downtime lasted only about two and a half hours. Besides questions about reliability, some doubters also voice worries about privacy and security.

But supporters of the cloud say that organizations like Salesforce and Google do a much better job of uptime and transparency than most IT departments. 'All complex systems have planned and unplanned downtime,' says Benioff, who claims 99.9% uptime last year. 'The reality is we are able to provide higher levels of reliability and availability than most companies could provide on their own.'

His 55,000 customers and 1.5 million subscribers, will be hoping that he is right.

Say if the following statements are TRUE (T) or FALSE (F).

1 Salesforce has been operating cloud services longer than the big players. ☐
2 Salesforce has had to change its business model because of falling profits. ☐
3 Benioff believes cloud computing will replace call centres and helplines. ☐
4 Cloud computing suffers from more unplanned downtime than average in-house IT departments. ☐

OVER TO YOU

- What applications do you regularly use that are provided in a "cloud"?
- Do you think people will be comfortable with all software being provided remotely in the future?
- What are your reasons for your answer?
- How many clouds will there be? Do you think one big service provider could provide a single cloud for everyone?

4 Networking

STARTER

Look at the map. What do you think the red lines represent? What do you think the blue shadows represent? Discuss your answers with a partner.

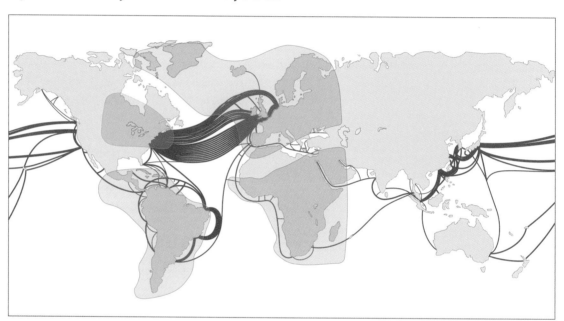

GLOBAL INFRASTRUCTURE

1   You will hear a call between Dave Wells, the telecoms manager of an oil company in London and Jerry Rigg, a geophysicist in charge of a small exploration team in West Africa. They are discussing the infrastructure that is available and how they will set up a local exploration office and communicate regularly with London.

These abbreviations appear in the extract you are about to hear. Think about how they are pronounced. Which one is the odd one out?

PTT   MPLS   PSTN   VSAT   DSL

TECH TUTORIAL

DSL = Digital Subscriber Line
Digital lines that are provided by telephone companies

PBX = Private Branch Exchange
A telephone system bought and used by a company in their office

PSTN = Public Switched Telephone Network
A country's telephone network

PTT = Public Telephone & Telegraph
A country's telephone network operator

VoIP = Voice over IP
Packetized voice over Internet

VSAT = Very Small Aperture Terminal
A small satellite dish normally mounted on the roof of a building

13

2 Listen to the extract and look at the diagrams. Tick (✓) the infrastructure that has been completed and is available. Cross (✗) the infrastructure that is still being developed or is being planned.

1 Submarine cable to Europe ☐ 2 Intelsat connection ☐

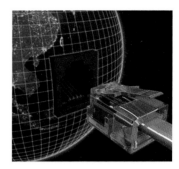

3 Global Ethernet services ☐

4 National fibre backbone ☐   5 Digital switching equipment ☐ 6 Fibre local loop ☐

3 Listen to the extract again. Complete this email with the words in the box.

infrastructure • capacity • local loop • redundant • data network • teledensity
• lead times • global Ethernet

Hi,
I've had a talk with Jerry about the telecoms _____ [1] that is available out there
and it's still pretty basic. On the plus side, there's a high _____ [2] fibre cable down
the west coast and the country is connected via Intelsat 1, so there are _____ [3]
connections, so basic emails and phone calls will never be a problem even if one of them
goes down.
However, at the moment there are no international _____ _____ [4]
providers out there so _____ _____ [5] services are not available. They
will be able to get a fixed line, but the _____ _____ [6] is just copper
and _____ _____ [7] are very long because _____ [8] is well
below average.
Best, Dave

4 From your knowledge of telecoms note three things that Jerry can easily do and three things Jerry can't easily do with the existing infrastructure.

When you have finished compare your notes with your partner.

5 Match the two part verbs in Column A with the meanings in Column B.

A		B	
1	put in	a	consider, think about
2	phasing ... out	b	discovered
3	dug up	c	get information about
4	rolling out	d	finishing with
5	look at	e	happening
6	going on	f	implementing
7	figure out	g	install
8	found out	h	taken out of the ground

6 Complete the sentences with the two part verbs from exercise 5.

1 We've been travelling around trying to _____ _____ what telecoms infrastructure is available.

2 What we have _____ _____ is that West Africa is connected to Europe

3 Some of the international data network providers are starting to _____ _____ expanding their networks

4 To its credit, the PTT is _____ _____ a national fibre backbone.

5 They are _____ _____ the old electro-mechanical exchanges.

6 Digital switching equipment is being _____ _____ the new exchanges.

7 So there's a lot _____ _____ at a national level.

8 The problem with the copper pairs in the ground is that they get _____ _____.

Listen to the extract again and check your answers.

7 Read this email from Mgumba to David Wells giving some information about the country's main telephone network. Complete the email with the words in the box.

PSTN • digital • twisted copper pair • VoIP • electro-mechanical   fibre • PTT • regional • PBXs • local

---

To: Dave Wells   ✉ From: Mgumba Batswana

Subject: The PSTN & Voice Services, In Country

Dave

I've done some digging for you. The _____¹ was of course based on analogue technologies. Most of the equipment in the old exchanges was _____² but this started being phased out five years ago. Digital equipment was installed in all the _____³ exchanges first and now 100% of intercity traffic is digital. Dialling codes exist for each city. There are still some _____⁴ exchanges that are analogue but these are switching over to _____⁵ at about one per month. The local loop/last mile is predominately _____⁶ but fibre is available for large offices in city centres. Lead times are a minimum of 30 days for copper and 90 days for _____⁷, if available. The _____⁸ does install and maintain digital _____⁹ for businesses. Their range can grow to about 500 extensions and two switchboards. I have only noticed one provider talking about _____¹⁰ services.

Mgumba

---

8 Make notes on the most important changes in the last few years that have affected:

a your country's PSTN (Public Switched Telephone Network). Think about:
  • equipment in local and regional exchanges.
  • the rollout of fibre.
  • broadband speeds.

b your own use of voice calls. Think about:
  • your use of landlines.
  • the price of calls.
  • your use of mobile technology.
  • your use of VoIP.

Compare your notes with your partner.

ENTERPRISE NETWORKING

9 **Read this article from Big Oil's internal magazine about their experience in West Africa. As you read, number the order in which these things happened.**

a The company set up a 100Mb Ethernet LAN. _____

b The team were given satellite phones. ___1___

c A contractor fitted out the office with CAT5 cabling. _____

d The company installed a private fibre loop to the new MPLS node. _____

e The company installed VoIP and teleconferencing applications. _____

f A global data networking provider extended WAN services to the capital. _____

When Big Oil started its search for oil in West Africa, their geophysicists carried out surveys to see whether there were any oil reservoirs underground. These surveys produced a lot of data which needed to be sent back to Head Office, but how do you transfer half a gigabyte of data out of the jungle when the local telecoms infrastructure isn't up to it, or not there at all? We talk to Dave Wells, Telecommunications Manager at Big Oil, about these challenges.

'The geophysicists who went out there first used sat-phones to transmit voice and data. But of course once the decision to drill was made, we had far more users to support with various requirements in a proper office environment.'

Big Oil's telecoms team is used to providing global voice and data connectivity into remote locations, says Dave. 'We worked with one of the global data networking providers to extend their WAN services here and convinced them to put an MPLS node into the capital. This meant they had a local presence and it allowed us to connect to their global network. We then had 8Mb connectivity from the router in my comms room in London down to the capital. We decided to pay to dig a trench and lay our own fibre local loop to give us reliable, high capacity bandwidth to our new premises.'

'A local contractor wired out the office with CAT5 cabling. We installed and remotely manage our own LAN hub and run a 100Mb Ethernet LAN around the building to laptops and PCs which have the same specifications and applications as London. We decided against a standalone PBX because we had a full 8Mb for voice, data and video traffic. We set up our 30 staff with VoIP and teleconferencing applications on their computers and they use headsets for their voice calls. This all works well, and from the traffic analysis we can see that they actually videoconference with London more often than just talk because of the infrastructure we put in for them.'

Despite being remote, the team on the ground now have the same capabilities as London, another example of how telecoms and IT can support businesses that operate in hard-to- reach places.

10 Read the text again. Say if the following statements are TRUE (T) or FALSE (F) according to the text.

1 The geophysicists did not find evidence of underground oil reservoirs.
2 Dave Wells said the new office only needed satellite phones.
3 A global networking provider opened a new facility in the capital.
4 The exploration office installed its own local loop.
5 The LAN in the exploration office is managed from London.
6 The staff in the exploration office make all their calls via their computers.

11 Read the text and find a word or phrase that means:

1 A person who is in charge of a company's telecommunications.
2 An organization that provides international telecommunications and internet access.
3 A network that covers a wide area such as a city or country.
4 A point where a connection can be made to an MPLS network.
5 A cable which allows a user to connect to a local exchange or node.
6 A network in an office or home that links different computers together.
7 A common connection point for devices in a local network.
8 A private telephone exchange that serves a business or office.

RELATIVE PRONOUNS

We can use the relative pronouns **who, which, where, when,** and **that** to describe and define.
We use *who* for people:
*The geophysicists **who** went out there first used sat phones.*

We use *which* for things:
*These surveys produced a lot of data **which** needed to be sent back.*

We can use *that* for people or things:
*Telecoms and IT can support businesses **that** operate in hard-to-reach places.*

We can use *where* to mean *in which, on which,* or *to which.*
*We looked for a building **where** we could set up an office.*

We can use *when* to refer to times, days, weeks, months, etc.
*We had several days **when** communication with London was very difficult.*

---

12 Complete these definition using *who, which, that, where,* or *when.*

1 A satellite phone is a kind of phone …
2 A geophysicist is a scientist …
3 CAT5 cabling is a kind of wire …
4 A Telecommunications Manager is someone …
5 An internet café is a place …
6 A bank holiday is a day …

13 Practise using these relative pronouns in a short game.

PARTNER FILES   Partner A   File 4, p. 75
Partner B   File 4, p. 77

NETWORK MANAGEMENT

14 Listen to the telephone call between a Big Oil Network Operations Manager and a remote employee in the exploration office. They are trying to locate a network fault.

Complete the left-hand column of the trouble ticket with the words below in the right order. See the example.

Ethernet cable and port • IP address • LAN hub • network card • ping test • power
• round trip delay • router • VPN

Big Oil Network Fault Management	Trouble Ticket Number 2574
User Name	Florence Knight
Contact Numbers	Office +219 1 356 5011 Mobile +219 7831 565889
Email Address	fknight@bigoil.com
Summary	User has lost voice and data connectivity to her PC this morning
1 *Power*	Yes / No
2	Connected / Unconnected
3	Functional / Non Functional
4	Tested / Untested
5	Visible / Invisible
6	Responding / Unresponsive
7	10.223.44.867*
8	Successful / Unsuccessful
9	Acceptable / Unacceptable
Trouble Ticket	Open / Closed

*In order to avoid using an IP address in use we have used a fictional IP address. Real IP addresses consist of four numbers ranging from 0 to 255 separated by dots.

15 Listen again and cross out the correct words in the right-hand column.

16 Complete the word puzzle to find the hidden expression. Listen to the extract again if necessary.

1 Florence tells Greg that she has lost voice and data _____.
2 Greg tell her that he will walk her _____ a series of tests.
3 First of all he asks her if there is _____ to the PC.
4 He asks her to check that the Ethernet cable is _____ in.
5 He doesn't bother to check the LAN _____.
6 It's clear that the LAN is _____.
7 Greg says that the VPN network _____ OK.
8 Greg can see the _____ on his network management application.
9 The problem is that the network card is not _____.
10 Greg asks her to reboot her _____.
11 Greg says he will _____ her network card with a ping test.
12 Greg carries out a round trip delay test to check that _____ is acceptable.
13 At the end of the conversation, Greg closes the _____.

17 Work with a partner. Role play two calls to sort out technical problems.

PARTNER FILES   Partner A File 5, p. 76
Partner B File 5, p. 78

Read the article about networking developing countries and answer the questions below.

As developing countries seek to upgrade their telecoms networks, they are faced with difficult choices.

On the one hand, they have the advantage of being able to forget about rolling out national fixed line networks. In some countries, teledensity is as low as 4%, so expanding a wired network to cover an entire population is far too expensive. The result is that they can bypass an old technology and move straight to a national wireless network to provide broadband and voice (VoIP) services.

On the other hand, there is a difficult choice to make – Wi-Max or 3G?

In many developing countries, Wi-Max (Worldwide interoperability for Microwave Access) has already made a huge impact. It delivers high-speed access wirelessly, enabling fixed and mobile broadband services over large coverage areas. It is an IP-based system and comes in two versions, fixed and mobile. Fixed Wi-Max is suited for delivering wireless last mile access for fixed broadband services, similar to DSL. Mobile Wi-Max supports both fixed and mobile applications with improved performance and capacity while adding full mobility. In India, Tata has launched what it says will be the world's biggest Wi-Max network, with a projected cost of $600 million.

In the other corner is 3G (and coming soon, 4G and LTE), a well-established wireless network in developed countries. 3G has evolved from the voice-centric telecoms world, but is able to deliver not just voice but high-speed broadband access as well. The last ten years have seen the growth of huge networks in the developed world, and emerging nations are catching up rapidly. China is investing billions of dollars in rolling out a nationwide 3G network that will reach 70% of the population, and the Asia Pacific region expects to have over 500 million 3G subscribers in the next few years.

In the longer term, we are already starting to see the convergence of Wi-Max and 3G. While Wi-Max has broadened to become more mobile and capable of being used for media services, 3G cellular has become increasingly broadband, resulting in practical convergence between these fields of development. What's more, both are driven to use the same core sets of technologies.

At the moment, developing countries still have to make a choice between the two systems, and are faced with the familiar Betamax vs VHS or BluRay vs HD decision. But if the two technologies can co-operate rather than compete, then the future of broadband and voice services in developing countries will look a lot brighter.

1   Why are some developing countries *not* developing their wired networks?
2   What suggests that Wi-Max and 3G are equally suitable for developing countries?
3   According to the text, what will happen to Wi-Max and 3G in the future?

OVER TO YOU

• What wireless technologies are being used in your country?
• What are the limits to wireless technology when compared to fixed line?
• Can you see the world becoming entirely wireless in the future?

5

Data centres and security

STARTER

LOCATION, LOCATION, LOCATION

Look at the pictures. Write down one advantage and one disadvantage of each place as the location for a Tier 4 (most secure) data centre. Compare your answers with a partner.

1

Peshawar, on the Pakistan/Afghanistan border

2

Industrial development zone, New Orleans

3

Business park, near Heathrow airport, London

4

Remote farmland, Ireland

DATA CENTRES

AUDIO
15

1 Rupert Wilson, CIO of a small investment bank, is visiting a German data centre to find out about the services they offer. Helmut Schwartz is taking him on a tour of the data centre. Listen to the first part of Helmut's tour and say if the following statements are TRUE (T) or FALSE (F).

1 The data centre is in a German city. ☐
2 The centre is closed for four days a year. ☐
3 Security at the centre is extremely tight. ☐
4 Senior managers do not need to follow all the security rules. ☐
5 The data centre is connected to two different network POPs. ☐
6 The centre always uses its own independent power supply. ☐

2 Listen to the talk again. Complete the notes about what Helmut says, adding at least two items for each section of the diagram. See the example.

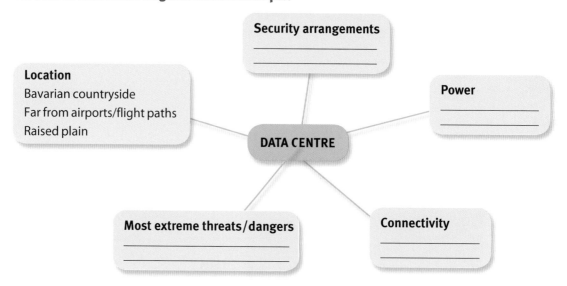

Security arrangements
_____
_____

Location
Bavarian countryside
Far from airports/flight paths
Raised plain

Power
_____
_____

DATA CENTRE

Most extreme threats/dangers
_____
_____

Connectivity
_____
_____

AUDIO
16

3 Listen to the second part of the tour. Match the words in the box with items 1–10 in the diagrams.

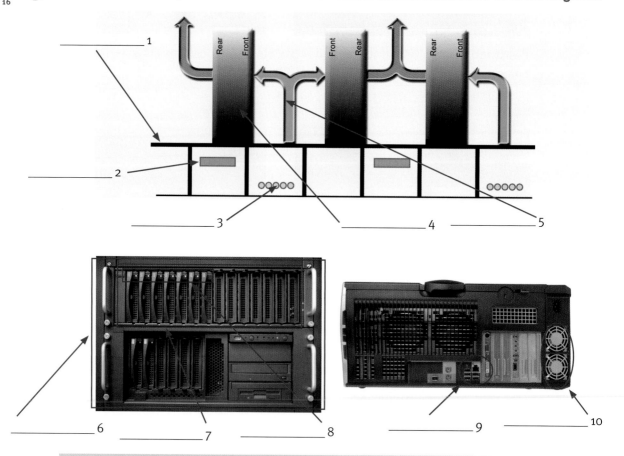

19-inch rack • alarm LED • blades • telecom cable trays • cold aisle • cabinets • raised, perforated tiles • power cables • Ethernet port • fans

4   **Match the words 1–11 from the listening with the definitions a–k.**

1	mission critical	a	sections of a centre sealed off from other sections
2	redundancy	b	using physical characteristics (e.g. fingerprints) for ID
3	downtime	c	one weakness that could stop an entire system
4	compartments	d	time when the equipment is not functioning
5	resilience	e	duplication of equipment in case one part fails
6	separacy	f	extremely important
7	network outages	g	ability to withstand unexpected problems or setbacks
8	power feeds	h	lack of electricity
9	power cuts	i	sources of electricity
10	single point of failure	j	having different and unconnected cables to a network
11	biometrics	k	times when a network is not functioning

Now work with a partner. Ask and answer questions using some of the words above.

1   In your work, what sort of data is mission-criticial?
2   How important is redundancy for the protection of data?
3   What elements do you think are important for the resilience of a Tier 4 data centre?
4   How might a Tier 1 data centre differ from a more secure one?

AUDIO

17

5   **Listen to the discussion Helmut and Rupert have after the tour. For questions 1–5, choose the correct alternative (A or B).**

1   Rupert says he:
    A   is keen to start outsourcing as soon as possible.
    B   has concerns about making such a big decision.
2   Rupert wants to know:
    A   what would happen if there was downtime during a trading period.
    B   if it is possible to avoid downtime completely.
3   Helmut tells Rupert that:
    A   they have never had any management problems.
    B   they have never had a comms outage.
4   According to Helmut, a power outage:
    A   would not cause any disruption.
    B   could be fixed in a matter of minutes.
5   The mirror site in Switzerland:
    A   has a copy of all the data at the centre.
    B   would warn the centre about an earthquake.

TALKING ABOUT IMAGINARY SITUATIONS

We often use the second conditional to talk about possible situations.
*If there **was** a comms outage, we **would switch** to the backup service.*
*If we **lost** power, our own back up power systems **would start**.*

We can also use other structures to talk about imaginary situations.
***In the event of** one of your servers going down ...*
***Supposing** there was an earthquake or you got hit by a plane, what would happen then?*
***Should** anything terrible **occur**, you would need to have standby communications links.*
***If that were to happen**, you would switch over to the hot standby site.*

---

6 **Match scenarios in A with solutions in B to make second conditional sentences.**

A Scenarios
1 If one power feed failed,
2 If both power feeds failed,
3 If anyone unauthorized tried to gain access,
4 If one telecoms service lost connectivity,
5 If the air conditioning went wrong,
6 If there was a problem with one of the servers,
7 If there was a complete catastrophe like an earthquake or a plane crash,

B Solutions
use / other network POP
temperature alarm / go off
isolate /change / straight away
be stopped / security guards
switch / mirror site / Switzerland
use / other power feed / grid
UPS system / generator

Now, work with a partner. Ask and answer questions about the scenarios.
Example:

A *What would happen if there was a long power outage?*
B *If we had a long power cut, we would use our own generators.*

7 **Work with a partner. One of you is an IT manager looking for a secure data centre, the other is a representative of a data centre. Role play the meeting.**

Partner A   File 6, p. 76
Partner B   File 6, p. 78

AUDIO
18

BANKING SECURITY

8 You are going to hear Jon, a bank security officer, answer some questions about his job. Before you listen try to complete the sentences about bank security.

| spear • white-hat • worms • ping sweep • TCP/IP • certificates |

1 A _____ hacker is a hacker who helps organizations protect themselves against criminal hackers.
2 A _____ is a process to check to see who is connected to a network.
3 _____ fingerprinting gives information about what operating system people are using.
4 128bit SSL _____ encrypt data.
5 Anti-virus software can protect against viruses and _____.
6 _____ phishing is a more targeted form of phishing.

Now listen to Jon and check your answers.

9 These were the questions that the interviewer asked Jon. Listen again and match the questions 1–6 to Jon's answers A–E on the CD. There is one question that was not asked.

1 What can people do to stay secure online? _____
2 Is there anything else that people should be aware of? _____
3 How do you go about that? _____
4 Is it safe to use credit cards online? _____
5 So, Jon, what sort of work do you do for the bank? _____
6 What's the difference between you and a normal hacker? _____

10 Read this short article about a computer infection.

Conficker has been in the news a lot recently. It is a _____[1], which unlike a virus does not need to be attached to an existing program to infect a machine, and which seems to receive regularly updated instructions from its controllers. It has created a _____[2] – a network of infected machines. Once infected, these machines are known as _____[3]. At this point no one knows what the purpose of Conficker is. At present it has infected ten million computers. These could be used for a _____[4] attack where all the infected computers attempt to access one site simultaneously.

It is probably controlled by criminals who want to steal users' personal information, i.e. _____[5]. There are a number of ways of doing this: a _____[6] records information entered via a keyboard, _____[7] literally means harvesting users' information while they are online. We will probably soon see if Conficker consists of this type of passive monitoring _____[8] or whether it will mount a more active attack once it receives a new set of instructions.

11 Work with a partner. Use the information in your Partner File to complete the text.

PARTNER FILES Partner A File 7, p.76
Partner B File 7, p.78

INFORMATION SECURITY

12 Read the introduction to an email and answer the questions.

1 Who is this email from (i.e. an employee, IT specialist, customer etc)?
2 Who is the email to?
3 What is the basic problem being discussed?
4 What will the rest of the email be about?
5 What kind of ideas might be in the rest of the email?

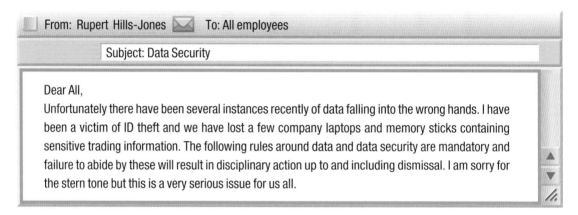

From: Rupert Hills-Jones   To: All employees

Subject: Data Security

Dear All,

Unfortunately there have been several instances recently of data falling into the wrong hands. I have been a victim of ID theft and we have lost a few company laptops and memory sticks containing sensitive trading information. The following rules around data and data security are mandatory and failure to abide by these will result in disciplinary action up to and including dismissal. I am sorry for the stern tone but this is a very serious issue for us all.

13 Read the rest of the email from Rupert Wilson, CIO of London Investments. Some sentences have been removed from the email. Read the text and complete the gaps 1–6 with the sentences a–f below.

a Ideally this should contain both letters and numbers.
b Only company-provided and approved software may be used.
c At the end of each day, ensure that your desks are clear and all documentation or storage devices are in locked drawers.
d Do not leave them where they can be seen on the back seat of a car.
e IT will be running a webcast on how to do this next Tuesday 25th.
f Any documentation found lying around after the trading day will be destroyed. You have been warned.

Clear Your Desk
With immediate effect we will be running a Clear Desk Policy in the office.
_____1.

Shred
All unwanted printouts, photocopies, notes etc. must be put into the shredders that have been installed in each office. _____2.

Use Passwords
All systems must be accessed using a password. _____3. This password is secret to you and should not be shared with any other individuals.

Change Passwords

All passwords must now be changed on a monthly basis. If you think that your password has been compromised, call the IT Helpdesk immediately.

Don't Download

All laptops are to be scanned on a monthly basis by IT to check for spyware or malware. Under no circumstances should any programs be downloaded from the internet onto company laptops. _____ [4].

Emails

Do not open email attachments unless you know the originator of the mail personally and you are expecting an attachment of that type and name.

Keep Secure

All laptops taken out of the office either to clients' offices or to work from home must be kept secure at all times. _____ [5].

Memory Sticks

All memory sticks are now numbered. The IT Department will keep a list of memory sticks and who is responsible for them.

Encrypt

All data stored on memory sticks must be encrypted. _____ [6].

And on a personal note if anybody sees my wallet, could you please pop it into my office.
Regards
Rupert

Confidential. Internet communications are not secure and therefore London Investments does not accept legal responsibility for the contents of this message. This email and any attachments may be confidential. They may contain privileged information and are intended for the named addressee(s) only. They must not be distributed without our consent. If you are not the intended recipient please notify us immediately and delete the message and any attachments from your computer. Do not disclose, distribute or retain this email or any part of it. We believe but do not warrant this email and any attachments are virus free. You must therefore take full responsibility for virus checking.

14 **Match the verbs in A with the words in B to make expressions from the email.**

A		B
1	be	an email attachment
2	change	a document
3	download	a program
4	open	a victim
5	run	a webcast
6	scan	a laptop
7	shred	a password

15 Now complete sentences 1–7 with the expressions from exercise 14. You may need to make changes to the verbs.

1 Why can it be dangerous to _____ if you don't know who sent it?
2 Why is it important to _____ like a bank statement that contains personal information, and not just throw it away?
3 How often should you _____ or a desktop for spyware and malware?
4 Why can it be harmful to _____ from the internet and run it on your computer?
5 Why is it a good idea to _____ regularly even if there's no evidence it has been compromised?
6 What are the advantages of _____ as opposed to having training seminars?
7 Have you ever _____ of ID fraud?

16 Work in pairs. Ask and answer questions 1–7 above.

GIVING INSTRUCTIONS

We often use the imperative to give instructions:
Ensure *your desks are clear.*
Use *passwords.*
Do not leave *them where they can be seen.*

We can also use a passive modal to give formal instructions.
*Only company provided and approved software **may be used**.*
This password should not be shared with any other individuals.
*All laptops **must be kept** secure at all times.*
*Under no circumstances **should** any programs **be** downloaded.*

---

17 Use the language from the box above to write a short email to the members of staff of a company. Think of three or four bullet points under the heading. (*Phishing* is the fraudulent stealing of information about bank accounts, PIN numbers, passwords, etc).

How to avoid phishing
-
-
-
-

OUTPUT **Read the article about Telecoms and IT in finance and answer the questions below.**

The Impact of Technology on Global Stock markets

The period of time between a trade being initiated and its completion is called latency – a key parameter for everyone involved in trading.

Before technology was introduced, the average number of daily trades at the London Stock Exchange was 20,000, amounting to about £700m worth of shares changing hands. After the introduction of automated trading, the figure went up to a daily average of 59,000 trades. This year saw nearly £18bn of transactions in one day.

'The speed and volume of trading is much, much higher these days,' said Sebastian Kolksmann who works for London Investments in Frankfurt. 'Transaction flows are faster driven by end investors, by electronic trading, algorithms, and lower latency.'

'Time is money as they say,' commented Bob Sherunkle, a New York Trader for London Investments. 'If our technology gets me information a nanosecond faster than everyone else, I may be able to sell a stock quickly, a split second before its price drops, or I may be able to buy another stock before its price starts to rise and it's more expensive for everyone else. That's why we need the fastest connectivity, the quickest processing, and the lowest latency out of our systems.'

So where do all these data transactions happen? Each exchange will have its own data centre that stores all the historic and current trading data with inputs, buy and sell requests, or market information, coming from all over the world. Trading companies are now starting to host their own server equipment at the stock exchanges' data centres, providing sub-millisecond access to the trading systems and market data, thereby eliminating network latency.

For member firms that are connected to Stock Exchanges via 100 megabit IP connectivity, collocating their servers could reduce roundtrip trade execution and market data transmission times by another one and a half milliseconds. Typically transaction capacity at exchanges is around 20,000 continuous messages per second and end-to-end execution latency for a deal is from about six milliseconds to three milliseconds.

Watching all this going on in dealer rooms around the world are the traders, surrounded by numerous screens showing red and green numbers and banks of phones allowing them to receive instructions from their clients to buy and sell, and effect those requests using their computers or calling another trading house. Just one exchange such as London will have more than 100,000 screens connected directly or indirectly to its data centre and trading systems. Of course, some dealers may be really putting IP networking technology to good use and have the same data on their laptop screen, while they are sitting on a beach somewhere in the world, trading virtually.

1　What was the main effect of the introduction of automated trading?
2　Where are more and more trading companies now keeping their servers?
3　How many messages can typically be sent per second?

OVER TO YOU

- Do you think the technology mentioned in the article will mean the end of centralized stock exchanges such as London, Tokyo, and New York?
- What are the security risks of having so many sensitive transactions happening online?

6 Services

Look at the profiles of these organizations. For each one, note down at least one advantage and one disadvantage of outsourcing its IT requirements to a Managed Service Provider (MSP).

For each company, think about these questions:

- How complex are the company's IT and networking requirements?
- To what extent is technology a core competence of each company – is technology something linked to the company's business?
- How important are issues like privacy / confidentiality / security?
- Can the company support the cost?

Maxland is a real estate company that operates in Southeast Asia. It has recently acquired several smaller competitors and now has offices in every state. It contacts clients through local advertising, databases, emails and has details of every property for sale on its website.

The Dressing Room is a small boutique specialising in clothes and accessories for women. It is a family business with only one store and the proprietor has little knowledge of IT.

G-soft is a start-up company in Korea that is developing a range of language learning DVDs and games. The office has five programmers and there is a team of 15 other freelance software developers and language teachers who also work for the organisation.

Olympus Z1 is code name of an operation that gathers intelligence from a military base in the Eastern Mediterranean. The team intercepts radio and email communications and passes the details back to the security services.

MANAGED SERVICES

1 **ThaiManagement is a Managed Services Provider that offers three different levels of service to customers. Read the advertisement below and match the three levels with the word that best describes the service.**

Managed

Reactive

Proactive

2 **Label the services offered B – Bronze, S – Silver, or G – Gold.**

1 includes the supply of new equipment _____

2 deals with problems within four hours _____

3 offers a helpline during the day only _____

4 offers the services of a manager probably shared with other customers _____

5 is the cheapest _____

6 deals with faults only after they happen _____

7 has the shortest contract term _____

8 includes an optional buyback of equipment _____

Bronze

ThaiManagement's Bronze package includes:

- A freephone Helpdesk number for you to report all your faults during normal business hours
- Experienced service agents responding to your call within 30 seconds
- Management of your fault with our market-leading trouble ticket system
- Qualified field maintenance engineers who are fully trained and equipped to fix your faults
- A guarantee that we will respond to your fault by the next working day
- All available for a low-cost service fee payable monthly

* A minimum contract term of three years is required

Silver

ThaiManagement's Silver package includes:

- Same day response to technology faults reported to our Helpdesk
- Service agents will take your calls during extended business hours (seven days a week!)
- Proactive Fault Monitoring – our agents will test and ping your equipment and services on a regular basis to spot problems before you do
- Performance monitoring of your network to find any bottlenecks or cost-saving opportunities
- Monthly Service Reports allowing you to spot trends in usage and problem areas and plan better for the future
- A ThaiManagement Service Manager assigned to your account, responsible for your total service experience

* A minimum contract term of five years is required

Gold

ThaiManagement's Gold package includes:

- A dedicated team proactively monitoring your equipment & services for faults 24 hours a day, seven days a week
- A fast, four hour guaranteed response to all faults reported 24/7
- Performance and utilisation monitoring of all your network and applications to ensure users get the experience they want
- Real time reporting provided online, enabling you to see what's happening with your technology infrastructure at all times
- A dedicated ThaiManagement Service Manager just for your business
- Buyback of your existing infrastructure as part of the agreement
- Technology refresh on an annual basis during the service contract

* A minimum contract term of five years is required

3 Work in pairs or two teams to play the game. Student A (or Team A) should try to answer questions 1–7. Student B (or Team B) should try to answer questions 8–14. The first person (or team) to answer their questions is the winner.

Find words or phrases in the text that begin with the letters in the question. See the example.

Example: What *F.H.* is a place you can call for advice and help at no cost?

Answer: *F*reephone *H*elpdesk

Questions for Student A / Team A:

1   What F.M.E. means *experts who travel to a customer's premises to fix problems*?
2   What W.D. usually means *any day except the weekend*?
3   What T.T.S. is a method for managing and responding to faults that are reported?
4   What E.B.H. means *more than just 9 a.m. to 5 p.m.* (e.g. 6 a.m. to midnight)?
5   What S.D.A.W. means *every day*?
6   What M.S.A. is an agreement between a customer and a service provider?
7   What O.A.A.B means once a year?

Questions for Student B / Team B:

8   What P.F.M. means *looking for problems before they happen*?
9   What S.F. is the price a customer pays every month to receive benefits?
10   What M.C.T. is the shortest period that an agreement lasts?
11   What S.D.R. means *dealing with a problem within 24 hours or less*?
12   What M.L. is an adjective that means *best selling*?
13   What C.S.O. means *chances to save money*?
14   What T.F.S. are numbers that mean *all the time with no interruptions*?

4 An agent from ThaiManagement is talking about the service the company can provide. Complete the sentences with the words and phrases from the box.

buyback • dedicated • fix • ping test • proactive • response • service • monitor

1   We offer a _____ service, which means that we try to predict and prevent faults rather than react to them.
2   If we can't _____ a fault immediately, we will replace the equipment.
3   Under our _____ scheme, we purchase all the equipment you are currently using and then upgrade it as necessary.
4   We will run a _____ on your equipment regularly to check that everything is working properly.
5   You can have a _____ manager who will be personally responsible for looking after your business.
6   We offer a very fast _____ to any faults that you report to us.
7   We will _____ your network and equipment 24/7 to ensure that everything runs smoothly.
8   We offer a range of different _____ level agreements.

COMPARING ADJECTIVES

We compare one syllable adjectives and two syllable adjectives ending in *–y* by adding *–er* or *–est* (the end *–y* becomes an *–i*).
The Silver service is **cheaper than** the Gold service.
The Bronze service is **the cheapest**.
Letting a service provider manage your technology is **easier than** doing it yourself.

We compare longer adjectives with *more ... than* or *...the most ...*
The Silver service is **more expensive than** the Bronze service.
The Gold service is **the most expensive**.

We can also make comparisons with *as ...as*, without changing the adjective.
Equivalent: *The contract term is **as long** for Silver **as** it is for Gold.*
Negative: *The Bronze service is **not as good as** the Silver service.*
Qualified: *The Silver service is **almost as expensive as** the Gold service.*

There are a number of common adjectives that are irregular.

good	better than	the best
bad	worse than	the worst

5 **Look back at the four organizations in the Starter on page 48. Make comparisons about them using the words in brackets. See the example.**

The Dressing Room is _____*the smallest*_____ (small) company.

1   The Dressing Room's IT requirements are _____ (not complex) those of Maxland.

2   The Dressing Room is probably _____ (easy) to manage than the other organizations.

3   Maxland's website is probably _____ (big) than any of the others.

4   Maxland's employees are probably _____ (not/computer-literate) as the staff at G-soft.

5   Of the four organizations, G-soft probably has _____ (good) in-house IT specialists.

6   G-soft's web presence is probably _____ (not/extensive) as Maxland's.

7   At Olympus Z1, security is _____ (important) it is at G-soft.

8   In fact, at Olympus Z1, security is probably _____ (critical) issue.

6 **Look back at the three levels of service offered by ThaiManagement. Make comparisons about the Bronze, Silver, and Gold services using these words.**

1   comprehensive
2   suitable for a small business
3   high monthly fee
4   long service contract
5   fast response time
6   personal service

SERVICE LEVEL AGREEMENTS

7 **Look at the home page for InterAsia Car and make notes on:**

1 who InterAsia Car's customers probably are.
2 how InterAsia Car probably attracts most of its customers.
3 three ways in which a Managed Service Provider might be able to help InterAsia Car.

When you have finished, discuss your notes with a partner or in small groups.

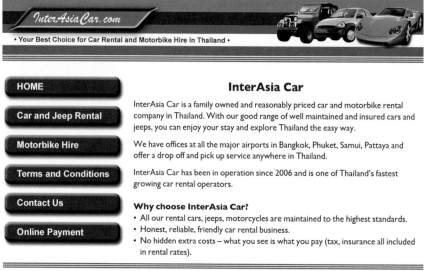

InterAsia Car.com

• Your Best Choice for Car Rental and Motorbike Hire in Thailand •

HOME

Car and Jeep Rental

Motorbike Hire

Terms and Conditions

Contact Us

Online Payment

InterAsia Car

InterAsia Car is a family owned and reasonably priced car and motorbike rental company in Thailand. With our good range of well maintained and insured cars and jeeps, you can enjoy your stay and explore Thailand the easy way.

We have offices at all the major airports in Bangkok, Phuket, Samui, Pattaya and offer a drop off and pick up service anywhere in Thailand.

InterAsia Car has been in operation since 2006 and is one of Thailand's fastest growing car rental operators.

Why choose InterAsia Car?
• All our rental cars, jeeps, motorcycles are maintained to the highest standards.
• Honest, reliable, friendly car rental business.
• No hidden extra costs – what you see is what you pay (tax, insurance all included in rental rates).

About Us | Site Map | Jobs & Opportunities | Links | Contact Us
© 2002 InterAsia Car, all rights reserved.

8 **The management team at InterAsia Car are having a meeting to decide what they might need from ThaiManagement. Chen the MD is talking with Anurak, his IT director and Betty, the Customer Service Manager.**

Read the comments they made about the table of services on page 53. Try to match the comments below with the rows a–i in the table.

1 It's important that we have it 24/7 like the Gold Service, but we don't need a dedicated team ... _____

2 Do we really need that – surely we're in the best position to know what needs replacing? _____

3 It's vital that we have cover seven days a week. _____

4 As long as there's someone who's familiar with our infrastructure, then I think a shared one would be fine. _____

5 If we have user or customer service problems because of our technology then we need to be able to see what's going on there and then. _____

6 Our applications are pretty simple; I don't think we need it for them. _____

7 ... we can manage that, no problem, but the Gold is more than double ... _____

8 ... we're very busy Saturdays and Sundays with people hiring cars at the weekend. We need at least the Silver Service ... _____

9 But boss, that means we'd lose control of our IT. _____

AUDIO
19

9 **Listen to the meeting to check your answers.**

AUDIO
20

NEGOTIATING AN SLA

10 Chen, the MD of InterAsia Car, is trying to negotiate a deal with Maliwan, the Sales Director from ThaiManagement. Listen to the dialogue. Circle the elements of the Silver Service and Gold Service in the table below that Chen and Maliwan agree on. See the example.

		BRONZE Service		SILVER Service		GOLD Managed Service
a	Maintenance Cover (Break/Fix)	✓	Next Working Day	✓	8 Hour Response	✓ (4 Hour Response)
b	Helpdesk Availability	✓	0900-1700 Mon-Fri	✓	0800-1800 7 days	✓ 24/7
c	Fault Monitoring	✗		✓	Shared Team Business Hours	✓ Dedicated Team 24/7
d	Performance Monitoring	✗		✓	Network Only	✓ Network & Applications
e	Reporting	✗		✓	Monthly	✓ Real Time Online
f	Service Manager	✗		✓	Shared	✓ Dedicated
g	Asset Buyback	✗		✗		✓ Cheque on Day 1
h	Technology Refresh	✗		✗		✓ Annual Upgrades
i	Monthly Price Per Unit		**7000 baht**		**16,500 baht**	**35,000 baht**

11 Listen to the extract again. Say who uses the following expressions. For Chen, write C, and for Maliwan, write M.

1 ... the SLA we are looking for is ... _____
2 We can manage that _____
3 The only thing is ... _____
4 How do you suggest we deal with that? _____
5 I'll have to think about that _____
6 How does that sound? _____
7 I'll meet you in the middle _____
8 Let's shake on that. _____

NEGOTIATING

Asking for suggestions
What can you do about that?
How do you suggest we deal with that?

Indicating a problem
Yes, but ...
The only thing is ..

Delaying a direct answer
I'll see what we can do.
I'll have to think about that.

Compromising
Let's compromise.
I'll meet you in the middle.

Asking for reactions to a proposal
Would you consider ...
How does that sound?

Agreeing
OK I don't have a problem with that.
OK that's not a problem.
I can accept that.
We can manage that

Talking about needs
We require ...
I'd like to talk you through what we are after.
What we are looking for is ...

Confirming an agreement
We have a deal
It's a deal.
Let's shake on that.

Give and take
If you ..., then I could ...
We can do that ..., but only if you also ...

---

12 **A customer is talking to an MSP. Put the following dialogue into the correct order. The first one has been done for you.**

a   Customer   *Hi, yes that's right. The website itself is fine, but what we are looking for is a way to cut costs a bit. How would you feel about reducing the monthly fee?*   ☐

b   Customer   *5% isn't that much but, OK, I can accept that.*   ☐

c   Provider   *All right, let's compromise – if you go for weekly updates, then we could cut the fees by 5%.*   ☐

d   Provider   *Great. It's a deal.*   ☐

e   Provider   *Hi, Jason, Mr Angelis said you wanted to talk to me about changes to the website.*   ☐ 1

f   Provider   *I'll have to think about that. The price you're paying at the moment is already very competitive.*   ☐

g   Customer   *Not really ... the thing is that we need it updated more than once a month.*   ☐

h   Provider   *Ok, then, we can probably give you something a bit more affordable if we cut some of the features. Would you consider monthly updates instead of daily ones?*

i   Customer   *Yes, I appreciate that, but the problem is that we really can't afford it, and I'm not sure we really need all the services you're providing.*   ☐

13 **Work with a partner. Look at the Negotiating phrases above and the information in your Partner File. Role play the negotiation.**

PARTNER FILES   Partner A   File 8, p. 76
Partner B   File 8, p. 78

Read the negotiating tips and answer the questions below.

5 Top Tips for Negotiations

These are tough times for IT. There are fewer people to get things done, budgets are shrinking and everyone still expects the same levels of service and functionality. But even in this tough, budget-conscious economy there are still some purchases that have to be made and contracts with Managed Service Providers that have to be renewed. So how do you ensure that you are getting the best value for money?

Martin Ewing is the principal at Pactoris, Inc. He has worked in the IT Industry for nearly 30 years and was the CIO of a multibillion dollar corporation before founding Pactoris in 2001. His company specializes in IT cost reduction and IT contract negotiations.

1 Get the Right People Involved

In today's complex world, technical skills and negotiating skills are both critical. Anyone negotiating software licensing, maintenance and other technology contracts needs to understand the details of the technology. Similarly, a negotiator needs procurement skills and enough experience to be comfortable with the negotiation process. Make sure that anyone talking to the vendor has both skills, even if it means getting outside help.

2 Fear, Uncertainty and Doubt (FUD)

Vendors are not frightened of purchasers any more, and some of the traditional hard-nosed procurement and negotiation methods no longer work. What makes vendors really uncomfortable is not knowing where they stand. So, say you are considering alternative solutions, but don't give out too much information. Hint at competition or alternatives, but don't threaten. Be as vague as possible and let them imagine the worst.

3 Get the Account Manager on board

We all know that you will only get big discounts if the senior management of the vendor's company approve. We also know that the person who best knows the approval system is the salesperson trying to sell to you. If they think they can get a sale by meeting your terms, they will become your best ally and most powerful weapon in getting you what you need. Let them do the work for you.

4 Know Your Options

There is always competition, even when negotiating maintenance contracts. The key is to convince the vendor that you have a serious alternative, because you do. There are companies that specialize in supporting third party applications, and there are also other alternatives, such as self-support, reduced coverage, block hours – the list goes on. And when it comes to hardware, there are still more companies that can provide the same or even higher levels of service at a significantly reduced cost. So make sure the vendor knows you're aware of your options.

5 Remember to Ask

Finally, the best piece of advice is very simple: Don't be afraid to ask for a better price. Just remember, if you don't ask – you don't get.

1 What two qualities does a good negotiator need?
2 What does the writer suggest instead of trying to appear tough and aggressive?
3 Why is the salesperson so important in getting you what you want?
4 Why are you *not* locked into maintenance contracts with a vendor?

- Do you think that one or two countries will end up dominating the telecoms and IT service sector providing services to the rest of the world?
- Why / why not?

7 Media

Look at the images of how different media can be used in advertising. Make notes on:

- **which forms of advertising are the most expensive.**
- **which forms of advertising you have personally responded to.**

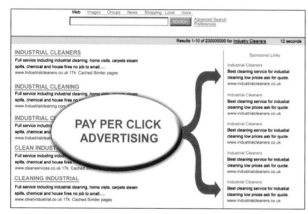

Pay per click advertising

TV advertising

Direct mail

Billboards

Now discuss your answers with a partner.

Read these situations. In each one, say which form of media the following people/organizations could use to contact their target audience (use your answers from the activity above and other ideas):

1. the owner of a holiday home who wants to advertise that the place is available to rent for part of the year.
2. a major manufacturer of confectionery who wants to promote a new chocolate bar.
3. a single person who has just moved to a new city and wants to make new friends and meet up with any old ones who may live in the area.
4. a cigarette company that wants to improve sales (direct advertising by tobacco companies is against the law, even on the internet).
5. a hardware company (with a database of customers) that wants to sell its latest notebook.
6. a supermarket that wants to warn customers that some tins of fish that it has sold recently may cause food poisoning.

`TELEVISION`

1 **Complete the table with details about you and your country.**

Who are the TV broadcasters?	
Who are the IPTV providers?	
What's the name of the TV service from the national PTT?	
How do you receive television?	
How many channels can you get?	
How do you pay for television – annual licence / monthly subscription / pay per view?	
How much do you pay (e.g. monthly TV costs compared to monthly telephone costs)?	
How have / will these amounts change?	

Now compare your answers with your partner.

TECH TUTORIAL

CRT = Cathode Ray Tube
The light source inside older TV sets
DRM = Digital Rights Management
Similar to copyright for electronic content
EPG = Electronic Programme Guide
An electronic list of programmes available on TV, cable, satellite, or the internet
IPTV = Internet Protocol TeleVision
Digital TV over a network

LCD = Liquid Crystal Display
The technology used in flat screen TVs and monitors
MPEG = Moving Picture Experts Group
A file format for audio and video
VOD = Video On Demand
Playback of video at request of user

---

2 **You are going to read a text about changes in television. Before you read, try to complete the notes on some of these changes. Complete the table with the pairs of expressions.**

> broadcast to all / download on demand • all scheduled / time shifted •
> antenna / broadband • TV licence or advertising / pay per view • CRT / LCD

	From	To	
to receive	_____	_____	1
to view	_____	_____	2
transmission	_____	_____	3
business model	_____	_____	4
schedule	_____	_____	5

3 Now read the text to check your answers.

PLAYING CATCH-UP

Until very recently television broadcasting had been mostly unchanged since the 1950s. Broadcasting has long used antennae to transmit images and sound using the radio spectrum. A receiving antenna, usually on the roof of homes, receives the signal and demodulates it to provide the sound and images to a cathode ray tube (CRT). Viewers had to watch programmes according to the transmission schedule set by the TV broadcaster and use a video tape recorder to view programmes that they missed.

But the rapid increase in digitization and broadband networking has changed all that. Now content makers large and small, old and new, can use the internet or IP networks to distribute content. IPTV can provide live multicast TV services to a number of users, normally subscribers to a service. A unicast VOD service provides the playback of video to the viewer's set-top box or computer.

The key advance that has enabled these services is the massive increase in low-cost broadband services into homes. In the past, lack of bandwidth restricted the use of video over the internet, but now content can be compressed into MPEG-2 or MPEG-4 formats, broken into IP packets and streamed across the networks into people's homes. Here it is decoded by a set-top box or played back with a media player on a PC. This is all having an impact on viewing habits. Presented with an EPG containing not only today's programmes but last month's, viewers can now watch things when they want to watch them, not when broadcasters want to transmit them. Even during a programme viewers can pause or rewind to see the goal they just missed, or listen again to the point made in a documentary. And if they do still miss a whole programme, they can record and store the data on the hard disk of their PVR (Personal Video Recorder).

Even the business models are changing, pay per view is already common and may yet replace the income from advertising or licence fees . Viewers are now watching content on LCD flat screens, PCs, or even mobile phones instead of bulky CRTs.

Two problems are created by all of these changes. Content makers worry that digital content is easily copied for free, although digital rights management provides some protection. Advertisers are now worried their content isn't watched at all as the viewers now have so much control they can fast forward through adverts.

4 Look through the text and find words that mean:

1 an aerial
2 the full range of radio frequencies
3 a piece of equipment that can decode digital signals for a TV set
4 a piece of software for playing audio and video files
5 a method of charging viewers based on what they watch
6 a fixed annual fee for owning a television set

5 Answer the following questions using some of the words above.

1 How does a traditional analogue TV signal get to a viewer's set?
2 How does a digital signal get to a user?
3 How can viewers record programmes or see what they have missed?
4 How can content providers or broadcasters make money from viewers?

6 Match the means of transmission to the definition. Then match them to an example of a leading provider from Britain.

a	unicast	1	closed transmission to a group of users	A	BBC
b	multicast	2	open transmission to anyone	B	YouTube
c	broadcast	3	transmission to a single user	C	Sky

Now think of an example of a leading provider from your country.

7 Look at these examples of words that can be used with the word *signal* or *content*. Complete the diagrams with words from the text on page 58.

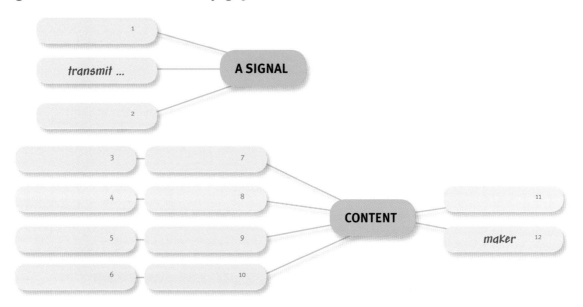

8 Complete these sentences using some of the expressions from exercise 7.

1 A lot of _____ _____ are concerned that their programmes are being copied illegally.

2 It is important for a national broadcaster to be able to _____ _____ to every part of the country.

3 MPEG techniques make it possible to _____ _____ into much smaller files.

4 A PC media player can _____ the _____ in MPEG, wmv and MP3 files.

5 Digital rights management allows film-makers to _____ _____ to a certain extent.

6 Most TV viewers still need an aerial pointing in the right direction to _____ _____ from the national broadcaster.

7 A CRT creates images from the _____ _____ it receives from the antenna.

8 As broadband capacities have increased, it has become easier to _____ _____ across networks in IP packets.

9 Mark each line with an X to show approximately where your country is on the spectrum of TV services. See the example.

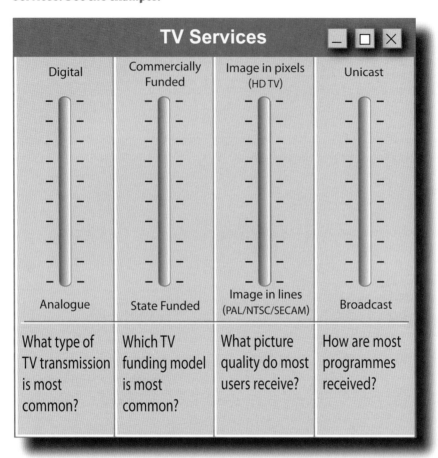

When you have finished, compare your answers with a partner and discuss the questions below.

- When do you think that TV transmission will be 100% digital in your country?
- Do you think that TV will ever be entirely commercially funded in your country?
- When do you think the choice of watching TV on a computer or accessing the internet via a TV will be irrelevant?
- Do you agree that the Unicast model causes fragmentation in TV viewing? What effect does this fragmentation have on the culture of TV on society when there are fewer big TV moments that large proportions of the population will have seen?

MEDIA START-UP

10 Start-up companies often need to raise money before they can launch a business. Make a note of one advantage and one disadvantage of each of the following ways of financing a new business:

	Advantage	Disadvantage

1 Using all your own money
2 Raising money from family
   and friends
3 Borrowing money from a bank
4 Raising money from a Venture
   Capitalist / Business Angel

When you have finished compare your notes with a partner. Discuss any real companies you know of that have raised money and explain what choices they made.

AUDIO
21

11 AdVentureUS are a venture capital company that specialize in funding international technology start-ups. You are going to hear three companies pitch for investment.

Listen to the first pitch. Complete the notes about the company and its business model.

Name: _____ 1
Main area of business: _____ 2

Revenue streams

_____ 3   Registered users after year 1: _____ 7
_____ 4   Registered users after year 2 : 5m
_____ 5   Registered users after year 3: _____ 8
_____ 6   Current stage of development: _____ 9

12 Complete the questions that an investor might ask with words from the box.

> account • banners • domain • e-commerce • hosting • mailing • messageboard
> • monetize • prototype • social

1 Are there any other _____ networking sites for pet owners on the net?
2 Who built the _____ that you are using to test out the idea?
3 How do you access the _____ to arrange walks with other local users?
4 How else could you _____ this and make it even more profitable?
5 How easy is it to register and create an _____ ?
6 What other products will you sell in the _____ section?
7 How much are you planning to charge for your advertising _____ ?
8 Who are you planning to sell the _____ list to?
9 How much did it cost to buy the _____ name?
10 Have you had any figures from the third party _____ company?

Now listen again to check your answers.

AUDIO
22

13 Note down answers to the questions in exercise 12 – use information from the text or invent any missing information. Now work in pairs.

Student A: You represent the venture capitalists. Ask the questions.
Student B: You represent Lamppost.com. Answer the questions.

14 Listen to the second pitch. Complete the notes about the company and its business model.

Name of company: _____ 1
Area of business: _____ 2

Main markets

_____ 3
_____ 4
Reason for needing funding: _____ 5
Time for product development: _____ 6
Time for testing and trialling: _____ 7

Income

Sign up fee: _____ 8
Monthly subscription: _____ 9
Sale of game in stores: _____ 10

15 Complete this email from one of the venture capitalists to a colleague.

consoles • controllers • graphics • joysticks • keyboards • networked • streamed • open source

Hi Jason
We've just had some people in to sell us an idea and I though I'd run it past you as this is more your field. Basically they've put together a team of _____ 1 video game developers to create a globally-_____ 2 war game that will be _____ 3 across the internet. This is aimed not just at people with games _____ 4 but also at PC users with a reasonable _____ 5 card, making the potential audience a lot bigger. My worry is that most PC users won't have _____ _____ 6 or game _____ 7 to move around the screen, but I'm not sure how important that is. _____ 8 are fine for typing, but how easy is it to control avatars with them?
Best, Alan

Now listen again to check your answers.

16 Make notes on which of the companies you would invest in and why. Discuss your notes with a partner.

WEBSITE USEABILITY

17 **Match the words with the definitions.**

1	jpeg / gif	a	a word, symbol, or image representing a company
2	a tab	b	an area that takes users to a separate page when it is clicked
3	block of text	c	an area of the screen with an advertisement
4	row	d	a vertical section of the screen
5	mock-up	e	a horizontal section of the screen
6	banner	f	commonly used formats for photographs
7	logo	g	an area of the screen filled with words
8	column	h	a working model for demonstration or testing

AUDIO

23

18 **Listen to Juan from Lamppost.com talking to a designer. Match the features a–e with the correct blanks 1–5 on the screen.**

When you have finished, compare your answers with a partner.

19 Listen to the dialogue again. Say if the following statements are TRUE (T) or FALSE (F).

1 The designer has placed the logo at the top of the screen on the left. ☐

2 Juan does not want advertisements on the home page. ☐

3 The 'Resources' tab will take users to the blogs. ☐

4 Regular users will have to sign up every time they use the site. ☐

5 The site will have an e-commerce facility for subscribers. ☐

6 Users can send an email if they forget their password. ☐

7 JPEGs work better than GIFs. ☐

8 Users will be able to upload their profile details to the site. ☐

DESCRIBING A PLACE

Look at the words and phrases we can use to describe the positions of items on a screen.

In the top left hand corner	At the top	In the top right hand corner
Top left		Top right
At the top on the left		At the top on the right
	In the middle	
On the left	In the centre	On the right
	Centre screen	
In the bottom left hand corner		In the bottom right hand corner
Bottom left		Bottom right
	At the bottom	

---

20 Work with a partner. You each have a brief for the homepage of a website. Make a rough sketch of the homepage, do not show this drawing to your partner. Using the words in the Language Box and exercise 17, describe the website's home page to your partner and ask them to draw it.

When you have finished, compare the drawings.

 PARTNER FILES   Partner A   File 9, p. 76
Partner B   File 9, p. 78

Read the article about news and answer the questions below.

MANAGING NEWS IN THE DIGITAL AGE

I am in the head office of a leading Spanish newspaper, standing in the cavernous News Hall, a vast circular room where the silence is only broken by the quiet hum of the air conditioning. All around, monitors flicker on individual desks, and high above is a giant screen that continuously streams news feeds and headlines from around the world.

My host, the editor Fernando Sanchez, takes me through the process of gathering news in the digital age. The newspaper's reporters are spread across the globe, some in diplomatic capitals, some in centres of commerce and some in dangerous trouble spots. More often than not they work either individually or in very small teams, relying on a simple combination of laptops, smartphones and digital cameras, although reporters in war zones have sat phones as well.

Like a one-man-band, each reporter can send digital material to a site that feeds into the production system. The 600 editorial staff receive this constant stream of news content along with reports from the Press Association, Reuters and other outside agencies. The editorial team, all Mac and Adobe users, then create the headlines and stories and get them ready for the print version or the internet.

The same news goes on both the newspaper and the website. The print version is sometimes scaled down and shortened for the daily publication; fuller pieces appear on the website, a 24/7 operation where the content is constantly changing.

In terms of information and data, the news operation manages hundreds of terabytes. The organisation has two data centres for disaster recovery reasons, each with a few hundred servers. The website gets about 240 million page impressions a month, and there are 30 million unique users split between Spain and Latin America.

As for the future, Mr Sanchez is confident that the paper will continue to prosper. 'The world is changing so fast,' he explains, 'and people are generating and receiving news in so many ways now - print, email, web, blogs, Twitter, it just doesn't stop. If a news business like ours is going to survive, we have to adapt quickly and embrace new technology. And believe me, that's just what we intend to do.'

1   How has technology changed the size of teams of reporters?
2   Apart from its own reporters, what sources does the newspaper use?
3   How does the print version of the paper differ from the online version?
4   To what extent is Mr Sanchez worried about the effects of new technology on the news industry?

OVER TO YOU

- Are printed, daily newspapers going to disappear? What are your reasons?
- What will the media landscape look like in five or ten years time in your country?
- Should music or other digital content be free?

8 Society

Read the quotes about technology.

The factory of the future will have only two employees, a man and a dog. The man will be there to feed the dog. The dog will be there to keep the man from touching the equipment.

Warren G. Bennis

Technology shapes society and society shapes technology.

ROBERT W. WHITE, 1990. (S&S)

The purpose of medicine is to prevent significant disease, to decrease pain and to postpone death... Technology has to support these goals – if not, it may even be counterproductive.

Dr Joel J. Nobel

When I took office, only high energy physicists had ever heard of what is called the Worldwide Web.... Now even my cat has its own page.

President BILL CLINTON

Computing is not about computers any more. It is about living.

Nicholas Negroponte

For a list of all the ways technology has failed to improve the quality of life, please press three.

Alice Kahn

The real danger is not that computers will begin to think like men, but that men will begin to think like computers.

Sydney J. Harris

Discuss the quotes with a partner.

- What do they say about the relationship between society and technology?
- Do you agree or disagree with them?
- Do you find any of them funny?

HEALTHCARE

AUDIO
24

1 You are going to hear part of a weekly radio programme called 'Technology Today'. The subject of this week's extract is healthcare. Listen to the introduction and match the people with their roles.

1	Lynn	a	Hospital manager
2	Malik	b	paramedic
3	Imogen	c	nurse on cardiac ward
4	Helen	d	patient
5	Sue	e	doctor in Accident and Emergency

AUDIO
25

2 Listen to the rest of the recording. For each person, <u>underline</u> two items that they mention.

1	Lynn	GPS	laptop	Sat Nav
2	Malik	database	wireless LAN	mobile phone
3	Imogen	CT scan	X ray	DICOM
4	Helen	RFID tag	digital clipboard	VoIP

3 Listen to the recording again. Complete the sentences with the missing words or phrases.

1 She _____ the emergency services, speaks to the _____ and asks for an ambulance.

2 The ambulance will _____ her Health Number ahead, and with that, all her details can be _____ from the National Patient Records Database.

3 The whole hospital will be _____ _____ so that with the correct security, actually a _____ _____ and password, doctors or nurses will be able to _____ a patient's records wherever they are in the hospital.

4 I would visit her every day, and _____ _____ to the hospital systems using my _____ clipboard. The clipboard would recognize the _____ tag in Sue's wristband.

5 She would then plug it into a _____ _____ and the data would be _____ to a database in the hospital and added to her patient records. The _____ would automatically display the data in a graph.

4 Write short sentences to describe how the following pieces of technology were useful in Sue's treatment and care.

1 GPS location
2 Radio
3 National Patient Records Database
4 Wireless LAN

5 Data tablet
6 RFID tag
7 Barcode reader
8 Remote monitoring device

Now, discuss your answers with a partner.

THE PASSIVE

We often use the passive voice to describe processes, especially if we are more interested in the action itself than in the person who does the action. It is formed using the verb *to be* and the past participle. We can use *by* at the end of the sentence to say who or what does the action.
Look at these examples from the extract:
*The hospital **is connected** to a national data network.*
*We **are directed** to the patient automatically **by** the sat-nav using the most direct route.*
*She **was brought** in to hospital*
*All her details **were downloaded** from the National Patient Records Database*

The passive can be used in most tenses.
Present Continuous
*She **is being treated** for shock.*
Future
*The new system **will be installed** on the NHS network.*
Present Perfect
*The patient **hasn't been examined** yet.*

The passive can also be used with modal verbs.
*He **mustn't be given** penicillin.*
*Medical records **can be downloaded** onto a laptop.*

---

5 Complete the summary of Sue's experience after her illness. Change the active verbs in brackets to the passive. Use *by* if someone's name is mentioned. See the example.

When Sue fell ill, (they rushed her) *she was rushed to hospital*, and (they gave her)
_____ ¹ emergency treatment as soon as she arrived. Then (they moved her)
_____ ² to K ward, where (Helen looked after her) _____ ³. (She visited her)
_____ ⁴ every day, and (she monitored her progress carefully) _____ ⁵.
(She recorded all the details of Sue's treatment) _____ ⁶ on a clipboard, and (someone transmitted the information) _____ ⁷ to Sue's digital patient records.

Now Sue is back at home, where (they monitor her) _____ ⁸ remotely. (A special device measures her heart and blood pressure) _____ ⁹ which transmits the data to the hospital, where (someone adds it) _____ ¹⁰ to her patient records. (Someone displays the data)
_____ ¹¹ on a graph for the doctors to look at, and if she needs more medication, (someone sends it out) _____ ¹² automatically.

SURVEILLANCE

6 Read through the statements. For each item, say to what extent you agree or disagree.

1 = agree strongly
2 = agree
3 = not sure
4 = disagree
5 = disagree strongly

Big Brother is watching you

1 The police should have everyone's DNA on their database.	1 2 3 4 5
2 I am in favour of CCTV cameras because they help to reduce crime.	1 2 3 4 5
3 The government should have the right to record everyone's internet activities	1 2 3 4 5
4 The authorities should have the right to intercept anyone's telephone conversations.	1 2 3 4 5
5 Biometric identity cards would be useful in the fight against terrorism.	1 2 3 4 5
6 It's OK for data about personal shopping habits to be collected and shared.	1 2 3 4 5
7 We need more traffic cameras with number-plate recognition to make the roads safer.	1 2 3 4 5
8 Law-abiding citizens need not worry about personal data that is collected about them.	1 2 3 4 5

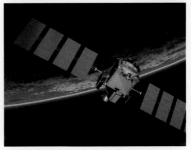

When you have finished, discuss your answers with a partner.

7 **Read the extract from a science fiction book on page 71.**

Do you think it is fictional?
Where do you think it is set?
Which of the methods of surveillance mentioned in the text are used in your country?

8 **Read the text again. Find at least eight occasions when personal information is taken or used. See the example:**

Recording/surveillance agent	Details taken
1 _Traffic cameras_	_Time of leaving in the car and arriving_
2 _____	_____
3 _____	_____
4 _____	_____
5 _____	_____
6 _____	_____
7 _____	_____
8 _____	_____

9 **Match the words from A with their meanings from B in the context of the story.**

A		B	
1	observing	a	made a note of
2	recorded	b	given permission
3	calculate	c	Internet company
4	provider	d	watching
5	logged	e	work out
6	authorised	f	recorded and written down
7	tagged	g	knew what (he) looked like
8	tracked	h	electronic till
9	recognised	i	stored and filed
10	archived	j	followed
11	EPOS terminal	k	fitted with a tracking device

10 **You are attending a conference on surveillance in London for five days. You are staying at a hotel near the conference centre. As part of the conference you have been set a practical task. You must remain completely unobserved, digitally, for the next five days, while still attending the conference and other meetings.**

Work with a partner and decide what you will do about:

- avoiding CCTV cameras
- money
- paying hotel and restaurant bills
- security equipment at the conference centre
- keeping in touch on the phone
- sending and receiving emails to your Head Office
- travelling round London

It was another grey morning as Winston set out on the journey to the train station. He kept glancing at the speedometer, making sure that he did not creep over the limit, knowing that the cameras were always observing him. They had already recorded his number plate at the start of journey and would be able to calculate if he had been speeding.

"At the next junction, turn left" the expressionless voice of the GPS called out, even though he had been making the same route for 15 years.

Under the watchful eye of the CCTV, he found a space in the station car park a safe distance from a small gang of youths. As he locked the car, he remembered that the home broadband contract needed renewing. He quickly phoned his wife on his mobile, explaining that the provider would know what package would suit them best as they knew how much data the family used. His presence in mobile cell D2-H21 was logged at 7.49.

He bought a Travel Card, and he was waiting for his credit card to be authorised, he noticed one of the CCTV operators in the back office pointing to a young man on the screen. It was one of the gang that Winston had noticed, and he was flashing up as being tagged.

This, however, was none of his business, so he bought the daily paper and waited patiently until the train slowly rolled in. The train was not full, so he settled down in a seat to send a few emails to his secretary on his Smartphone. He avoided any sensitive words that the GCHQ computers would notice, but knew that the messages would be stored for 12 months anyway.

The train jerked slowly into the grey city station, and the passengers got off. Winston followed his standard route, down into the tube, three stops along the Circle Line and up again in Western Road as 102 cameras along the way tracked his every move. His face was not wanted by the National Criminal Database; when he arrived at the Department, the biometric scanner in the foyer recognised him and the alarms remained silent.

The morning passed uneventfully. The few calls he made and emails he sent were digitally recorded and archived for three years, and at lunchtime he left for a brisk walk in the park. On the way back, he stopped at a bookshop to buy a book on Left Wing Politics, using his loyalty card to get a discount. The system noted that he should be sent details of this month's special offer, and the bank database informed the EPOS terminal that there were sufficient funds in the account.

After an uneventful day at the office, he was making his way back to Western Road when his wife called him in cell A56-Z88 at 5.38.

"Winston, you couldn't get a takeaway for this evening could you – there's nothing in the house and I've been out all day.'

"Yes of course – see you soon."

The Golden Lotus was just around the corner. The familiar smell of Chinese food met him as he swung open the door and saw Lee Ho Weng behind the counter.

"Ah Mr Winston, nice to see you again. Another takeaway, yes? Let's have a look at what you ordered last time.'

22

TECHNOLOGY ADOPTION IN SOCIETY

11 A favourite topic of internet blogs and chat rooms is technology flops, i.e. technology that hasn't been a success. Read this comment thread about why some technology flops and some unexpectedly takes off and becomes very successful.

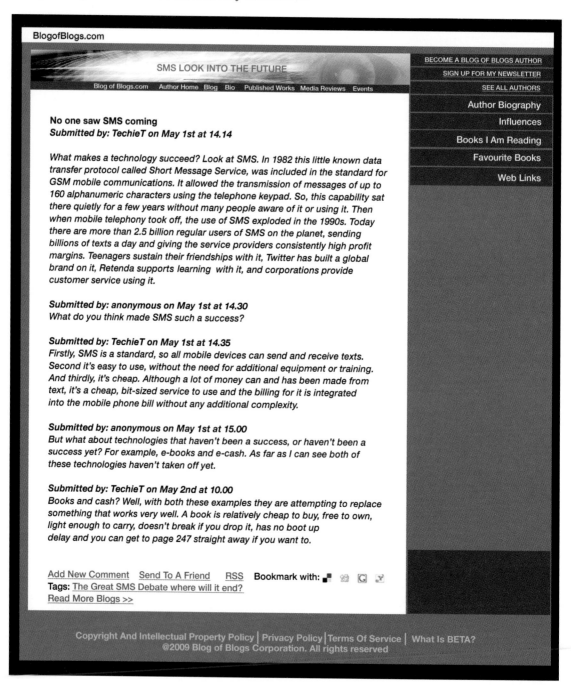

BlogofBlogs.com

SMS LOOK INTO THE FUTURE

Blog of Blogs.com   Author Home   Blog   Bio   Published Works   Media Reviews   Events

BECOME A BLOG OF BLOGS AUTHOR
SIGN UP FOR MY NEWSLETTER
SEE ALL AUTHORS
Author Biography
Influences
Books I Am Reading
Favourite Books
Web Links

No one saw SMS coming
Submitted by: TechieT on May 1st at 14.14

What makes a technology succeed? Look at SMS. In 1982 this little known data transfer protocol called Short Message Service, was included in the standard for GSM mobile communications. It allowed the transmission of messages of up to 160 alphanumeric characters using the telephone keypad. So, this capability sat there quietly for a few years without many people aware of it or using it. Then when mobile telephony took off, the use of SMS exploded in the 1990s. Today there are more than 2.5 billion regular users of SMS on the planet, sending billions of texts a day and giving the service providers consistently high profit margins. Teenagers sustain their friendships with it, Twitter has built a global brand on it, Retenda supports learning with it, and corporations provide customer service using it.

Submitted by: anonymous on May 1st at 14.30
What do you think made SMS such a success?

Submitted by: TechieT on May 1st at 14.35
Firstly, SMS is a standard, so all mobile devices can send and receive texts. Second it's easy to use, without the need for additional equipment or training. And thirdly, it's cheap. Although a lot of money can and has been made from text, it's a cheap, bit-sized service to use and the billing for it is integrated into the mobile phone bill without any additional complexity.

Submitted by: anonymous on May 1st at 15.00
But what about technologies that haven't been a success, or haven't been a success yet? For example, e-books and e-cash. As far as I can see both of these technologies haven't taken off yet.

Submitted by: TechieT on May 2nd at 10.00
Books and cash? Well, with both these examples they are attempting to replace something that works very well. A book is relatively cheap to buy, free to own, light enough to carry, doesn't break if you drop it, has no boot up delay and you can get to page 247 straight away if you want to.

Add New Comment   Send To A Friend   RSS   Bookmark with:
Tags: The Great SMS Debate where will it end?
Read More Blogs >>

12 Complete TechieT's comment about e-cash.

technophobes • niche • factor • proprietary • standard • user-friendly • barriers

As I said about SMS, for a technology to take off, it's a real advantage if there is a _____¹ that everybody uses. _____² technology owned by one company often has a hard time as the competition can make life difficult. For e-cash to work it's no good it only appealing to a _____³ segment of the market, – early adopters, it's also got to be accepted by _____⁴, people who really don't like technology. There are other _____⁵ to the adoption of e-cash, think about cost, security, and think about all the changes banks and shops would have to make. Usability is a critical ____ _____⁶ that cannot be ignored. There might be a day soon when we reach a tipping point and e-cash becomes more _____⁷ than hard cash.

OPINIONS

Saying what you think	Agreeing	Disagreeing
I think that ...	Absolutely.	Well, that may be true, but ...
It seems to me, ...	That's right.	Well, you may have a point, but ...
I'd say that ...	That's just what I was thinking.	I see what you mean, but ...
As I see it ...	I agree entirely.	No, but the point is ...
The important thing to remember is that ...		No, look, ...

13 Complete the sentences with your opinion on the technologies mentioned in the comment thread.

1   I think SMS will _____.
2   In my opinion e-books will _____.
3   From my point of view e-cash will _____.

Now discuss your opinions with a partner.

14 Choose the technology you know most about from the list below or choose another technology you know about. Write a blog post with your opinion about the present and future of this technology.

Unified Communications
The paperless office
Virtual Reality
Speech Recognition
Smart Appliances

15 Exchange your post with a partner. Write a comment in response to your partner's blog post.

OUTPUT

Read the article about Green IT and answer the questions below.

Green IT

The world's ICT carbon emissions are thought to be about equal to the emissions of the aviation industry, about 2% of the global total. A search on Google emits about 7g of CO_2. The amount of electricity required to send, read and delete all the spam email in the world could power 2.1 million homes instead. In the US alone 426,000 mobile phones are thrown away every day.

Conversely, using videoconferencing between London and Tokyo instead of flying for a meeting would stop you generating 4.2 tonnes of carbon. It's predicted that good use of telecommunications and IT could actually reduce other industries' carbon emissions by 7.8 billion tonnes. That's five times telecommunications' and IT's own carbon footprint.

So what does best practice look like if we are to make sure our telecommunications and IT usage is as green as possible? As in the example above, using video conferencing and telepresence equipment and services to reduce travelling to meetings, or teleworking from home, have a hugely beneficial impact on the travel-related carbon that we produce. Allowing computers to run "smart" buildings, where the heating, cooling, ventilation and lighting are managed as economically as possible, is another positive application of digital technologies.

But our equipment itself needs to be as efficient as possible. Datacentres use huge amounts of electricity to power chips that generate lots of heat, and more power is needed to cool them down. Datacentres could be made greener in many ways, for example by being built in locations with lots of sunlight so they could be powered by solar energy. Alternatively, if datacentres are produce so much heat, perhaps it could be used to heat homes. At a user level there are other initiatives like Blackle, which highlights that black computer screens and white letters would use less power. Black screens use about 59 watts of power compared to white screens that use 74 watts.

Then we come to the end of a product's life and how we dispose of millions of tonnes of computers, screens, mobiles, smartphones and cables each year. Europe has had the WEEE Directive (Waste Electrical and Electronic Equipment Directive) since January 2007 to encourage everyone to reuse, recycle and recover electrical and electronic equipment. The directive places the responsibility, and associated costs, of disposal onto the manufacturer or the user. This result is that equipment is now being designed and made to last longer; when it is thrown away and replaced by the latest model, much of it can be recycled and sent to developing countries, where it can be used again.

1   In what ways is the telecoms and IT industry bad for the environment?
2   In what ways could the telecoms and IT industry be good for the environment?
3   How could user equipment be made greener?
4   In what two ways has the WEEE directive had positive results?

OVER TO YOU

- How green is your own use of Telecoms and IT?
- Do you think digital technology has improved society?
- How do you think technology could help society in the next 50 years?

| Partner A | **Partner Files** |

UNIT 1, Exercise 20   File 1

You are an expert in the field of Artificial Intelligence and Artificial Life. Tell your partner about your predictions in your field. You are very certain about your predictions in the near future but less certain about predictions in the more distant future.
- AI entity gains entry to University – 2015
- AI entities given basic 'human' rights – 2018
- Computers more intelligent than humans – 2020
- Living genetically engineered teddy bear – 2040
- Robot team beats England football team – 2050

UNIT 2, Exercise 3   File 2

You are a history student. You have noticed that a lot of your fellow students bring computers to lectures. You'd like to have one but you are not sure what to get. These are your needs:
- You make notes on paper and use your PC at home to write longer assignments.
- Your university campus is covered by Wi-Fi.
- You can access all your course information via an online Learning Management System.
- You have to walk two miles to get to university.

UNIT 3, Exercise 19   File 3

Complete the table with the workstreams below. You will not be able to complete all of them.
- June 21st: Migrate to new system (one week)
- June 3rd: Sign contract
- Last week of August : Project Handover
- Agree Terms and Conditions before Contract Signature

When you have finished, ask your partner questions to complete the remaining information in the table.

UNIT 4, Exercise 13   File 4

You each have three pieces of equipment. Take turns describing your equipment to your partner. You must NOT use any of the forbidden words beside each picture.
Example

Telephone
Forbidden words: Telephone, phone, landline

This is a fairly traditional piece of fixed equipment that you can use to talk to friends or colleagues in another office on the other side of town or even in another country. It is not the sort of thing that you can carry around in your pocket, because it is too big. The older versions of these had a circular dial that had the numbers 1 to 0, and later versions had push button numbers.

mp3 player
Forbidden words: iPod, mp3 player

USB stick
Forbidden words: USB stick, memory

RJ 45 Connector
Forbidden words: RJ 45 Connector, Ethernet

	May				June				July				August				September				October			
Week	1	2	3	4	1	2	3	4	1	2	3	4	1	2	3	4	1	2	3	4	1	2	3	4
Workstreams																								
Terms and Conditions																								
Contract Signature																								
Design Phase																								
Migrate to New System																								
Testing Period																								
Project Handover																								
Sign Off																								
Steady State																								

UNIT 4, Exercise 17   File 5

1 **Student B will call you to talk about a technical problem. Ask questions to complete the trouble ticket below.**

Trouble Ticket Reference	
User Name	
Contact Numbers	Office
	Mobile
Email Address	
Summary of Problem	
Power	Yes/No
Ethernet Cable & Port	Connected / Unconnected
LAN Hub	Functional / Non Functional
Network Card	Responding / Unresponsive

2 **Now call Student B to try and solve a technical problem. Answer Student B's questions using the information below,**
- Your ticket reference from when you first reported the fault is 2003.
- You can't make voice calls.
- Your headset appears to be OK.
- The telephony application on your PC is not locked up.
- You can see that your IP address is 10.778.23.199*.
- Your volume is turned down which is why you can't hear anything. When you turn it up it works.

*This is a fictional IP address.

UNIT 5, Exercise 7   File 6

You are the IT Manager of VCVQ, a small but growing Venture Capital company. At the moment all your data is held on a server at your main, unsecured office, but you are concerned about whether the system is suitably resilient and any loss of data would cause your business some serious problems. Speak to Student B, a representative from Data Safe and Sure, a nearby data centre services provider, who provides services for SMEs in your area. You might need to invent additional information.
In particular, find out:
- the advantages of hosting your data and applications in their data centre.
- how secure the data centre is.
- how resilient the data centre is.
- how the transfer of data would be managed from your servers to the data centre.
- what types and levels of service they offer.
- what the price would be if you signed up.
Once you are satisfied you have enough information, decide which of Data Safe and Sure's offers you want.

UNIT 5, EXERCISE 11   File 7

Complete gaps 1–4 in the text on page 43 with the words below.

denial of service   BotNet   worm   zombies

Now ask your partner questions to complete gaps 5–8. For example:
What is stealing users' personal information known as?

UNIT 6, Exercise 13   File 8

You work for the Bangkok branch of the estate agency Maxland (see page 48). You have arranged a meeting with Student B, who is from ThaiManagement.
Look at the services that ThaiManagement can provide for your business (see page 49) and then decide which five features of the Gold service are the most important to you.
As you are not going to need all the features of the Gold service, you only want to pay 20,000 Thai Baht per month.
Role play the negotiation to get as many services for the best price.

UNIT 7, Exercise 20   File 9

Sketch a homepage for a website that relies on advertising for its income. You need to make sure that it has space for sponsored banners and links to other websites.

Partner B | Partner Files

UNIT 1, Exercise 20   File 1

You are an expert in the field of Biotechnology. Tell your partner about your predictions in your field. You are very certain about your predictions in the near future but less certain about predictions in the more distant future.

- Plastic bones – 2016
- Nano devices implanted in blood – 2017
- Electronic memory enhancement – 2020
- Virus crosses from machines to humans – 2025
- Artificial brain – 2045

UNIT 2, Exercise 3   File 2

You are a graphic design student. You need to update your computer. These are your needs:

- In class, you use the university computers.
- You need to handle and store large image files.
- You need a fast, reliable broadband connection.
- You need multiple windows open at the same time.

UNIT 3, Exercise 19   File 3

Complete the table with the workstreams below. You will not be able to complete all of them.

- Design phase from Contract Signature until June 20th
- Testing Period from June 28th until Handover
- Steady State from September onwards
- September 1st: Sign Off

When you have finished, ask your partner questions to complete the remaining information in the table.

UNIT 4, Exercise 13   File 4

You each have three pieces of equipment. Take turns describing your equipment to your partner. You must NOT use any of the forbidden words beside each picture.

Example

Telephone
Forbidden words: Telephone, phone, landline

This is a fairly traditional piece of fixed equipment that you can use to talk to friends or colleagues in another office on the other side of town or even in another country. It is not the sort of thing that you can carry around in your pocket, because it is too big. The older versions of these had a circular dial that had the numbers 1 to 0, and later versions had push button numbers.

Laptop
Forbidden words: Laptop, notebook

Portable speakers
Forbidden words: Portable, speakers

Home wireless router
Forbidden words: Wireless, Router

Week	May				June				July				August				September				October			
	1	2	3	4	1	2	3	4	1	2	3	4	1	2	3	4	1	2	3	4	1	2	3	4
Workstreams																								
Terms and Conditions																								
Contract Signature																								
Design Phase																								
Migrate to New System																								
Testing Period																								
Project Handover																								
Sign Off																								
Steady State																								

UNIT 4, Exercise 17   File 5

1 **Call Student A to try and solve a technical problem. Answer Student A's questions using the information below. You can give your own name, email address and phone numbers.**
   - Your ticket reference from when you first reported the fault is 7708.
   - The problem you have is that you cannot send or receive emails.
   - You have power.
   - Your Ethernet cable is connected.
   - Your LAN hub isn't working.
   - Your network card is OK.

2 **Now Student A will call you to try and solve a technical problem. Ask questions to complete the trouble ticket below. Decide whether to close the ticket or leave it open for further investigation.**

Big Oil Network Fault Management	Trouble Ticket Number 2003
Summary of Problem	
Headset	Damaged / Undamaged
Telephony Application on PC	Locked Up/Functioning
IP address	
Headset Volume	On/Off
Trouble Ticket	Open/Closed

UNIT 5, Exercise 7   File 6

You are the representative of Data Safe and Sure, a data centre services provider and have been called to a meeting with Student B, the IT Manager of VCVQ, a small but growing Venture Capital company. Answer Student A's questions, You need to find out:
- how secure their data is at the moment.
- what would happen if there was a fire / flood / break-in / hardware failure or loss of power or communications.
- explain the advantages of using your data centre which has been purpose built.

Once you have enough information explain that you have two basic offers:

Full service
You host and manage all their applications and data and provide a service monitoring service 24/7 and 365 days per year. This costs £1000/GB per annum

Back-up service
You keep an up-to-date copy of their data in case they have a problem. A remote backup is done once a day that costs £50 a week for no more than 1GB of data backed up.

UNIT 5, Exercise 11   File 7

Complete gaps 5–8 in the text on page 43 with the words below.

pharming   spyware   keylogger   identity theft

Now ask your partner questions to complete gaps 1–4. For example:
What is the difference between a virus and a worm?

UNIT 6, EXERCISE 13   File 8

You work for ThaiManagement. Student A, who works for the Bangkok branch of the estate agency Maxland (see page 48), has come to see you to discuss managed services.
Student A only wants some of the features of the Gold Service (see page 49). After discussing the matter with your boss, you have decided that each feature of the Gold service is worth a monthly fee of 6000 Thai Baht.
Role play the negotiation to get the best price for as few services as possible.

UNIT 7, Exercise 20   File 9

Sketch a homepage for a website that relies on subscriptions for its income. You need to make sure that visitors will want to stay on the homepage and let them know that there are advantages to signing up and paying the subscription.

Answer key

UNIT 1

page 4

STARTER
Suggested answers
phone, email, music, radio, TV, calendar, calculator, spirit level, maps, games, camera, photos, watch, business finder, English tests, internet, stock market feed, weather, text, movies

4
1 b   2 c   3 a

5
1 F   2 F   3 F   4 T   5 F   6 F   7 T   8 F   9 F

6
1 b   2 e   3 c   4 d   5 a

7
1   mobile phones
2   Silicon Valley
3   download a demo version
4   go online
5   access (their) accounts
6   silicon chip

8
2   are listening
3   cheaper and cheaper
4   more and more sophisticated
5   is getting longer and longer
6   is taking over
7   are increasing

9
Upload, upgrade, update
Downtime, download
e-book, email, e-commerce
teleworking, teleconferencing, telecoms
cyberspace, cybercrime

Hardware, adware, spyware
Waveband, broadband, narrowband
Broadcast, podcast, newscast
Smartphone, cellphone, i-phone, headphone
Kilobyte, megabyte, gigabyte

10
1   teleworking
2   cybercrime
3   gigabyte
4   downtime
5   spyware
6   upgrade

11
1   cellphone, upgrade
2   broadcasters, download
3   software, telecoms
4   update, gigabytes
5   telecoms/teleconferencing, broadband

12

Which speaker...	1	2	3	4	5
manufactures hardware	✓				
manufactures traditional software			✓		
provides a search engine				✓	
provides SaaS (software as a service)				✓	✓
enables voice telephony			✓		✓
provides TV		✓			✓

14
broadband pipe
data centre
digital camera
disruptive technology
internet access
search engine
service provider
voice calls

15
1   service provider
2   voice calls
3   broadband pipe
4   data centre
5   disruptive technology
6   internet access
7   search engine
8   digital camera

16
red line = telecoms
blue line = software/hardware
green line = business
yellow line = society

17
1 d   2 a   3 g   4 f   5 b   6 e   7 c

19
1   Windows probably won't remain the dominant force in software.
2   People may stop using cash by around 2015.
3   The mouse is bound to disappear in the next few years.
4   Mobile phones will probably be replaced with something different.
5   The rate of change definitely won't slow down.

OUTPUT
1   smartphones
2   $20
3   over the Internet
4   31%
5   9 months
6   24

UNIT 2

page 14

1   1 f   2 a   3 e   4 c   5 d   6 b

2

SuperMob 360: GSM, GPS, GPRS, email, internet, 1GB, 8hrs battery
SilverLite: Full keyboard, wireless broadband, Wi-Fi, Bluetooth, 2.5kg

5

Warehousing: no idea what's in stock, being delivered
Tills: old, don't work
Customer service: staff too busy, bad service

6

1 renewal	5 converged
2 chain	6 stock
3 continuous	7 schedules
4 terminals	8 trends

8

1 are manufacturing	5 depletes
2 rollout	6 shrinkage
3 display	7 legacy
4 purchased	8 off-site

9   Suggested answer

… and the system will be able to order goods automatically if they need replacing. This means that the problems of running out of stock will be a thing of the past.
All the goods will be tagged, and this means that we will be able to track exactly where they are, making it easier to deliver better customer service.
I know we have had problems with the tills, and all of these are to be replaced by state-of-the-art EPOS touch screen terminals. With the new tills, we will be able to check stock levels, answer customer enquiries, and even suggest alternatives.
Finally, we will have a centralized call centre for customer service and special mobile phones for staff on the shop floor.
We are looking forward to the new system and are sure that these improvements will enable us to deliver excellent value and even better customer service in the future.
Best wishes,
…

10

1 RFID	6 bluetooth
2 attachment	7 upload
3 device	8 warehouse
4 EPOS	9 supply chain
5 enabled	

Hidden word: inventory

11

1 c   2 b   3 a

12

1 c   2 d   3 a   4 f   5 b   6 e

13

1 T   2 T   3 T   4 F   5 F   6 T

14 Suggested answer

1   can attract customers near the premises; can target advertising;
2   can find products they like; can find the store they are looking for
3   increased competition from other outlets in the area; possibly an increase in cost
4   increase in spam messages on mobile phone; loss of privacy

OUTPUT

1 T   2 F   3 T   4 T

UNIT 3

page 21

2

1 customized	5 software licences
2 data format	6 helpdesk
3 upgrade	7 operating system
4 releases	8 applications

3

1 b   2 h   3 j   4 g   5 f   6 d   7 e   8 i   9 k   10 a   11 c   12 l

4

1   five
2   analyse
3   specification
4   software engineers
5   software architecture
6   bugs
7   customize
8   Project Manager
9   bespoke
10 off the shelf

6   1 iv)b   2 i)   3 iii)   4 iv)a   5 iv)c   6 ii)

7

1 consolidation	6 volume discounts
2 compatible	7 coordinated
3 capacity increases	8 functionality
4 incompatible	9 issues
5 vendors	10 integrate

8

1 functionality	4 capacity increases
2 issues	5 coordinated
3 compatible	6 volume discounts

9

OPTION 1
will last for three years
will only cost half of the other option
can be done in two stages
only requires one company to change its software
can be implemented over two years

OPTION 2
will last for seven years
will cost two years' profit
can be implemented in a year

11

1	Jan 21	5	Apr 1
2	Mustafa	6	HR
3	HR	7	June 14
4	Jane	8	September 24

12

1 February 22
2 March 15
3 April 8
4 May 3
5 October 29

13

1 F   2 F   3 T   4 F   5 F   6 T

14

1 c   2 h   3 a   4 f   5 b   6 g   7 d   8 e

15

1	slippage	3	deadline	5	bottleneck
2	stick to	4	rollout	6	dirty data

16

1	until	3	until	5	in	7	by
2	on, at	4	-	6	until	8	at

17

1 first of all   2 then   3 before
4 after that   5 finally

OUTPUT
1 T   2 F   3 T   4 T

UNIT 4

page 30

STARTER
The red lines represent submarine cables.
The blue shadows represent satellite footprints.

1

VSAT is the odd one out because the 'SAT' part is
pronounced as a word (that sounds like the first part
of *sat*ellite). The others just use the letters P, T, M,
etc.

2

1	✓	3	✗	5	✗
2	✓	4	✗	6	✗

3

1	infrastructure	4	global Ethernet	7	lead times
2	capacity	5	data network	8	teledensity
3	redundant	6	local loop		

4
Suggested answer
Jerry can easily:
1 make a call with the satellite phone.
2 send an email.
3 make a local call.

Jerry can't easily:
1 transfer large data files quickly.
2 use video or videoconferencing.
3 run a large office.

5
1 g   2 d   3 h   4 f   5 a   6 e   7 c   8 b

6

1	figure out	5	phasing … out
2	found out	6	put in
3	look at	7	going on
4	rolling out	8	dug up

7

1	PSTN	6	twisted copper pair
2	electro-mechanical	7	fibre
3	regional	8	PTT
4	local	9	PBXs
5	digital	10	VoIP

9
a 5   b 1   c 4   d 3   e 6   f 2

10
1 F   2 F   3 T   4 T   5 T   6 T

11

1	Telecommunications Manager	5	local loop
2	global data networking provider	6	LAN
3	WAN	7	hub
4	node	8	PBX

12 Suggested answers
1 … that connects by sending a signal up to a
  satellite in space.
2 … who studies both geology and physics.
3 … that you can use to carry internet signals.
4 … who is in charge of the PBX and IT at a company.
5 … where you can go to check your emails on
  holiday.
6 … when almost everyone has the day off.

14 and 15

1 Power	Yes / ~~No~~
2 Ethernet cable and port	Connected / ~~Unconnected~~
3 LAN Hub	Functional / ~~Non-Functional~~
4 VPN	Tested / ~~Untested~~
5 Router	Visible / ~~Invisible~~
6 Network Card	~~Responding~~ / Unresponsive
7 IP address	10.223.44.867
8 Ping Test	Successful / ~~Unsuccessful~~
9 Round Trip Delay	Acceptable / ~~Unacceptable~~
Trouble Ticket	~~Open~~ / Closed

16

1 connectivity
2 through
3 power
4 plugged
5 hub
6 functional
7 tested
8 router
9 responding
10 pc
11 check
12 latency
13 ticket

Hidden expression: trouble ticket

OUTPUT

1 too expensive
2 They use the same core sets of technologies.
3 They will be successful.

UNIT 5

page 39

Starter
Suggested answers

1 advantage: cheap, English speaking, well-educated labour
   disadvantage: terrorism
2 advantage: new development
   disadvantage: flooding
3 advantage: well-connected
   disadvantage: near airport
4 advantage: safe
   disadvantage: little infrastructure

1
1 F   2 F   3 T   4 F   5 T   6 F

2 Suggested answers
Security arrangements: CCTV, fencing, barriers, 24-hour security guards, daily security checks, biometrics between compartments

Power: Two separate power feeds, UPS system, generators

Connectivity: Two different network POPs, Two different carriers

Most extreme threats: plane crashes, bombs, malicious employees, men in diggers

3

1 raised, perforated tiles
2 telecom cable trays
3 power cables
4 cabinets
5 cold aisle
6 19-inch rack
7 blades
8 alarm LED
9 Ethernet port
10 fan

4
1 f   2 e   3 d   4 a   5 g   6 j   7 k   8 i   9 h   10 c   11 b

5
1 B   2 A   3 B   4 A   5 A

6 Suggested answers
1 … we would use the other power feed from the grid.
2 … the UPS system would kick in or we would use our own generators.
3 … they would be stopped by the security guards.
4 … we would use the other network POP.
5 … the temperature alarm would go off.
6 … we would isolate it and change it straight away.
7 … we would switch to the mirror site in Switzerland.

8

1 white-hat
2 ping sweep
3 TCP/IP
4 certificates
5 worms
6 spear

9
1 D   2 E   3 C   4 Not asked   5 A   6 B

10

1 worm
2 BotNet
3 zombies
4 denial of service
5 identity theft
6 keylogger
7 pharming
8 spyware

12

1 a manager
2 all staff
3 security
4 what can be done about the problem
5 using virus scans, spyware scans, changing passwords, locking rooms etc

13
1 c   2 f   3 a   4 b   5 d   6 e

14

1 be a victim
2 change a password
3 download a program
4 open an email attachment
5 run a webcast
6 scan a laptop
7 shred a document

15

1 open an email attachment
2 shred a document
3 scan a laptop
4 download a program
5 change a password
6 running a webcast
7 been a victim

17 Suggested answers
* Under no circumstances give confidential information to an email that claims to come from a bank
* Ensure that you change your password regularly
* Do not write down your PIN
* Your computer should be scanned regularly for viruses

OUTPUT
1 increased number of transactions
2 stock exchange data servers
3 20,000

UNIT 6

page 48

Starter Suggested answers
Maxland may well want to use managed services because:
* they need a strong web presence.
* they need up-to-date technology.
* IT is not one of their core competencies.
* their IT needs are complex.
* a managed service provider could give them better services and save money.

The Dressing Room is less likely to use a managed services provider because:
* the company is small and the IT requirements are simple.
* the owner may be reluctant to spend money.
* some IT operations (accounts, pay roll etc) may be already catered for by an accountant.
* on the other hand, the owner might outsource a website for the store.

G Soft may not outsource its IT operations because:
* IT skills are one of its core competencies .
* they already have creative and technical people.
* the company is relatively small.

Olympus Z1 will probably be reluctant to use a managed services provider because:
* they will be able to have their IT needs met by government or military experts.
* they need to maintain the highest levels of security.

1
Managed – Silver
Reactive – Bronze
Proactive – Gold

2

1	G	4	S	7	B
2	G	5	B	8	G
3	B	6	B		

3
A
1 Field Maintenance Engineers
2 Working Day
3 Trouble Ticket System
4 Extended Business Hours

5 Seven Days A Week
6 Managed Service Agreement
7 On An Annual Basis

B
8 Proactive Fault Monitoring
9 Service Fee
10 Minimum Contract Term
11 Same Day Response
12 Market Leading
13 Cost-Saving Opportunities
14 Twenty-Four Seven

4

1	proactive	5	dedicated
2	fix	6	response
3	buyback	7	monitor
4	ping test	8	service

5
1 not as complex as
2 easier
3 bigger
4 not as computer literate
5 the best
6 not as extensive as
7 more important than
8 the most critical

7 Suggested answers
1 They are probably tourists or visiting business people
2 It probably attracts them via the website or by advertising in travel and airline magazines
3 a It could ensure the equipment was functioning properly
  b It could optimize the website
  c It could automate the hiring, return, maintenance, and servicing of the car fleet

8
1c 2h 3a 4f 5e 6d 7i 8b 9g

10
They agree on:
Maintenance cover: 4-hour response
Helpdesk Availability 24/7
Fault monitoring: Shared team 24/7
Performance monitoring: Network only
Reporting: Real Time Online
Service Manager: Shared
Asset Buyback
Technology Refresh

11

1	C	5	M
2	M	6	M
3	C	7	M
4	C	8	C

12
1e 2a 3f 4i 5h 6g 7c 8b 9d

OUTPUT

1 procurement skills and experience
2 be vague
3 They know the approval system best.
4 There are alternatives.

UNIT 7

page 56

Starter
Suggested answers

1 advertise in a (paper) holiday magazine, the classified section of a daily newspaper or on a specialist holiday website.
2 launch an advertising campaign on TV
3 use a social networking website to contact old friends and meet new ones
4 tobacco companies face severe restrictions on advertising; in some countries, sponsorship of sporting events may still be possible.
5 launch an email advertising campaign as this would be relatively cheap and it has a database of customers
6 warn people by placing notices in daily newspapers; in addition, place notices in its stores and on the company website

2

1 antenna / broad band
2 CRT / LCD
3 broadcast to all / download on demand
4 TV licence or advertising / pay per view
5 all scheduled / time shifted

4

1 an antenna
2 spectrum
3 set top box
4 media player
5 pay per view
6 licence fee

5
Suggested answers

1 The signal comes over the radio spectrum to a rooftop antenna, then it is demodulated and sent to a CRT.
2 A digital signal can be compressed into MPEG2 or MPEG4 formats, broken into IP packets and streamed across the Internet.
3 They can use a video or HD recorder or use a VOD service.
4 Via a licence fee, subscription, or pay per view.

6

a 3 YouTube b 1 Sky c 2 BBC

7

1 receive
2 demodulate
3 distribute
4 compress
5 stream
6 decode
7 play back
8 watch
9 copy
10 protect
11 provider
12 maker

8

1 content makers/ content providers
2 transmit a signal
3 compress content
4 decode ... content
5 protect content
6 receive a signal
7 demodulated signal
8 stream content

10
Suggested answers

1 Using your own money:
Advantage: you remain in full control of the business
Disadvantage: your risk is much higher, the resources available may be limited
2 Friends and family:
Advantage: You still maintain good control over the company
Disadvantage: You are putting families and friends at risk; in the event of failure, there are personal consequences; funds may be limited
3 Bank financing:
Advantage: There is a chance of substantial funding if the business is successful
Disadvantage: The bank may charge a high rate of interest; in some circumstances, the bank may want to recall the money
4 Venture capitalist/Business Angel
Advantage: Business Angels may also give advice and help based on their own experience
Disadvantage: You may have to give away a large amount of equity in the business to secure the funding

11

1 Lamppost.com
2 social networking for dogs and their owners
3 registration fee
4 e-commerce section
5 advertising
6 mailing list
7 2m
8 15m
9 have built prototype and have had discussions with hosting company

12

1 social
2 prototype
3 messageboard
4 monetize
5 account
6 e-commerce
7 banners
8 mailing
9 domain
10 hosting

14

1 BigFight
2 gaming
3 games console users
4 PC users
5 support development activity
6 one year
7 six months
8 $10
9 $4
10 $39.99

15

1	open source	5	graphics
2	networked	6	joysticks
3	streamed	7	controllers
4	consoles	8	keyboards

17

1 f   2 b   3 g   4 e   5 h   6 c   7 a   8 d

18

19

1 T   2 F   3 F   4 F   5 T   6 F   7 T   8 T

OUTPUT

1 They have become smaller.
2 It is scaled down and shortened.
3 outside agencies
4 He is not worried.

UNIT 8

page 66

1

1 b   2 e   3 a   4 c   5 d

2

1	GPS	SatNav
2	database	wireless LAN
3	CT scan	DICOM
4	RFID tag	digital clipboard

3

1 dials, operator
2 radio, downloaded
3 wireless-enabled, swipe card, access
4 log on, digital, RFID
5 broadband adapter, transmitted, application

4

1 The GPS location equipment worked out which ambulance was closest to the patient's home.
2 The radio was used to send the patient's National Health number.
3 The database was used to download Sue's records.
4 The wireless LAN allowed the doctor to see Sue's records on the move.
5 The data tablet allowed the nurse to keep a record of the drugs Sue was given.
6 The RFID tag made sure Sue was given the right medication.

7 The barcode reader helped the nurse to check and record the drugs.
8 The monitoring device measured Sue's temperature, heart rate etc.

5

1 she was given
2 she was moved
3 she was looked after by Helen
4 She was visited
5 her progress was monitored carefully
6 All the details of Sue's treatment were recorded
7 the information was transmitted
8 she is monitored
9 Her heart and blood pressure are monitored by a special device
10 it is added
11 The data is displayed
12 it is sent out

7

It is not fictional and it is set in the UK.

8 Suggested answers

CCTV cameras	record his arrival and where he has parked
Mobile phone operator	record his presence in cell D2-H21
Broadband provider	has records of what data the family use
CCTV	notes that one of the youths is tagged
GCHQ	scans and archives emails
102 cameras	track his route to work/ check National Database
Biometric scanner	checks identity
Phone company	digitally records and archives calls
Loyalty card	records book purchases
EPOS terminal	checks bank balance
Phone company	records presence in cell A56
Restaurant computer	records details of purchases

9

1 d   2 a   3 e   4 c   5 f   6 b   7 k   8 j   9 g   10 i   11 h

12

1 standard
2 Proprietary
3 niche
4 technophobes
5 barriers
6 factor
8 user-friendly

OUTPUT

1 It uses a lot of energy and produces waste such as mobile phones.
2 It could be used for teleconferencing or for running 'smart' buildings.
3 use less power
4 Equipment lasts longer and can be recycled.

Transcripts

UNIT 1, EXERCISE 11

 Device Manufacturer

2   To be honest we don't know what to do these days. We used to make cameras and went digital. But then everybody wanted good cameras on cellphones, so we started making those, but people are always wanting to upgrade and get the latest models or new gadgets. I went to a technology fair last week and they were demonstrating this jacket and hat that was your phone. There are so many disruptive technologies, I don't know what's going to happen. Maybe we'll have to get into clothing.

 TV Broadcaster

3   A lot of broadcasters like us are having a hard time. The problem is that there are lots more channels these days and people also get them through different media. I can download the latest films from the phone company. My children don't even watch TV. They watch video online and their friends send them clips on their mobiles. But we have to survive on our advertising revenue and at the moment that's falling. Things are really not easy, and I'm sure there are some broadcasters that will go out of business.

 Software Manufacturer

4   We manufacture software, and we are doing really well at the moment – the telecoms service providers and telecoms equipment companies just can't compete with us. I mean, what's the point of having a phone on your desk nowadays when you can plug a headset into your computer and an application does all your voice telephony for you – and often for free? With a desktop computer, IP connectivity, and a headset, you don't need any PABX or all that voice cabling around the building or expensive maintenance contracts and so on. That's why our business is growing so fast and as far as I can see, it's likely to continue.

Search Engine

5   We run a search engine, so we're in a great position to take market share from both the software and hardware industries. What's the point in buying hundreds of software licences if your employees can just come to us and use one of our applications online? We provide security, we maintain and update the applications, we do all the data storage, archiving, and backup. Companies don't need to run data centres anymore, we do that. Employees don't need expensive laptops or desktops with gigabytes of RAM. They just need Internet access devices on their desk or in their hand. They can access the applications and data they need to from anywhere.

 Fixed Telecommunications Networking Provider

6   We own the fixed telecoms network, and we've seen a big fall in revenues from voice calls because everything is IP now. But in fact we're now in a great position because we are putting intelligence into our network so that it can become an enormous computer, capable of delivering applications. All our customers need is a broadband pipe into our network cloud and we act as an IT utility – and most people have already got that with an ordinary phone line. With the new capabilities we have, we can provide TV, software, Internet access, email, teleconferencing, all sorts of things – and that easily makes up for the money from traditional voice calls.

UNIT 1, EXERCISE 16

 It's very difficult to predict exactly how technology
7   developments will progress and indeed some of these predictions may have already happened by the time you listen to this, and some may still be a long way off.

What we will definitely see over the next few years is a very high rate of change because of the convergence of technologies. Convergence is far from over. The next twenty years will see much more of it, and the whole of IT will converge with the fields of biotechnology, nanotechnology, and cognitive technology. The result is that companies in every industry sector will see enormous changes. There will be great opportunities and of course great dangers as well.

If we look at telecommunications, today's trend for massive increases in bandwidth into people's homes means that providers will create different business models, so voice calls – and a lot else – are likely to be free in the very near future, say 2011. As for mobile technology, mobile phones have come from nowhere in the last ten years and now they are everywhere; but they'll probably disappear in another ten years. Instead of mobile phones we will probably have their functionality built into things like jewellery or patches, and information will be displayed on contact lenses. These could become available by about 2020.

The software industry is very likely to see big changes. Windows' market share will fall below 50% – perhaps as early as 2011 and definitely by 2015. We will also see software delivered as a service, and this will slowly become the norm. At the same time there will be big developments in hardware. We will see chips with ten billion transistors and they will lead to desktop computers that can compute as fast as the human brain by 2017. Forget the keyboard and mouse or even speech recognition as a way of inputting data. The next big development will be thought recognition, and that may be viable some time around 2025.

In terms of business, we may see paper money replaced by smart media as early as 2011. The technology is already there, but people or banks may not feel comfortable with it. Manufacturing, logistics, and retailing are very likely to replace all barcodes with RFID technology in the 2011 to 2015 timeframe.

And what will society look like in the future with all this digital technology? In some countries there is already a lot of surveillance and we are certain to see this grow into most neighbourhoods by 2014. And as surveillance in the real world grows, we'll see more and more virtual reality, but that too will bring its own problems, and virtual reality escapism may start becoming a social problem around 2015. Most societies will have ID cards by 2016 but even these will probably be replaced by biometric scanning within a few years of that, so anytime from 2020 onwards.

So, it is clear that things like five-year IT investment plans for business are becoming almost pointless because things are changing so fast. Companies must learn to be adaptable: adaptability will be the main quality for survival, while going for efficiency today can lead to death tomorrow.

UNIT 2, EXERCISE 1

8

Kate	Morning, how can I help you?
Antonia	I need some suggestions on updating my mobile technology.
Kate	Tell me what you use at the moment and what you need to do and I'm sure that I'll be able to recommend something appropriate.
Antonia	Well, I run my own small business which has been going really well. I've got an old desktop and a GSM phone. The problem is that I'm on the move so much it's not very convenient only being able to access all my information when I'm in the office. I also have to make two or three long conference calls a week. The battery on my phone quite often runs out after these and it's a bit embarrassing charging my phone in a customer's office and it's not very professional.
Kate	That shouldn't be a problem. The battery life of devices these days is pretty impressive. What sorts of tasks do you need to be able to do when you're away from the office?
Antonia	Well, obviously, I want the basic functionality of my current phone. So to be able to make and receive voice calls and voicemail, conference calls, and so on. I send and receive emails all the time and sometimes I need to be able to read the attachments. It would great if I could access the database we have at the office just before I meet a client to check how their order is progressing so I can give them up-to-date information. Also, I need to update my calendar on a daily basis so that my PA

always knows where I am. I'd like to be able to do all these things on the move or if I'm working from home.

Kate	OK well, for a mobile professional such as yourself, the two main options that you have are either a mobile phone and a wireless laptop or a handheld device such as a smartphone. These are better than the old PDAs, which of course can't do voice. It really depends on how much weight you want to carry around and how often you create documents or do significant work on them out of the office.
Antonia	I don't mind carrying around something a bit heavier as long as I can do everything I need to do. I often have to create or amend documents or presentations when I'm away from the office, that's important to me.
Kate	OK, what I would recommend is this. For your voice requirements I'd go for this SuperMob 360 3G phone which is GSM and GPRS enabled for voice, data, and location-based services. It also has an email application on it and it's internet enabled so you can also browse the internet. 1 gigabyte of data transfer per month is included for the first year. More importantly, you will be able to access that database at your office to download customer orders. Actually, you could also use it to keep your calendar up-to-date as it could synchronize with your PA's desktop automatically. It has a battery life of eight hours and a spare so you should be able to go all day without needing to recharge, even with long conference calls. All the SuperMobs also have GPS so you'll be able to find your clients easily. There are now lots of applications you could download to it, depending on what you need. It would also be worth getting a laptop such as this Silver Lite A2 and use that instead of your desktop. A full keyboard will be much easier to use than the tiny keys on a handheld device. It has got wireless broadband and is WiFi enabled so you can use it in coffee shops, trains, or airports. It has also got Bluetooth so it can communicate with the phone if you ever needed it to. It comes with all the applications you need to work wherever you are. And at 2.5kg it's one of the lightest laptops on the market.
Antonia	Wow, that all sounds great. I wish I'd come in sooner. I'll take that combination please.
Kate	Great, I'll just check on the system to see if we have them in stock. One second. Oh dear, I'm so sorry we haven't got any in stock at the moment and I don't know when the next delivery is. I'm sorry.

UNIT 2, EXERCISE 5

Malcolm Hi this is Malcolm; please leave a message after the tone.

Bob Malcolm, it's Bob.

Look, I am really concerned about the lack of investment in the technology we have in our stores and this is causing us real problems. My sales staff are trying to sell our products to our customers without knowing whether they are in stock. They are spending a lot of time trying to find things in the warehouse that are actually out of stock. And we can see when popular products are running low but we haven't go an easy system to reorder and restock.

We can't see what's going out and what's coming in, so we haven't got a clue what's going on. We do not know which suppliers are going to be delivering goods and on which date. We have lorries from the distribution centre turning up at the store warehouse unannounced and we have no idea what inventory they are delivering, so we have to unpack it all to find out what it is, before we can store it in the warehouse. And because we are not sure what we are supposed to have in stock, we can't check to see if anything has been lost or stolen.

And then if we do manage to sell something and it is in stock, our next embarrassment to trying to work these old tills. Have you any idea how stupid we look selling the latest smart phone or laptop and then having problems at checkout because the tills don't work? You should see the queues.

And it gets worse. While my staff are looking for items in the warehouse, customers have to wait and some just walk out. The shop floor staff are also having to answer the phone, which is ringing all the time, when they should be serving customers.

Look – we are losing sales because we do not have the right goods in stock and our customers receive a terrible level of service. We're going to lose customers to our competition, Bob, if we don't sort this mess out soon.

The irony is, Bob, we are a technology retailer and yet our own technology is rubbish.

Can you let me know what IT is going to do about all of this?

UNIT 2, EXERCISE 12

Presenter So, as you know most smart phones these days are GPS enabled so their location can be monitored. This is useful for navigation and mapping or tracking your workforce.

But for us, as retailers, if we know where someone and their smart phone are, we can figure out which businesses and services they are near. If we also know what the user likes or dislikes, we can show or recommend places to them on their smart phone screen. This is known as GeoMarketing.

Antonia So if, for example, I sold high quality pizza, and the customer was registered somewhere as a pizza lovers then my shop would show up on their smart phone map?

Presenter Yes, that's correct

Antonia Cool. So how does that work then?

Presenter Well the location of the mobile device is calculated by timing signals sent by satellites to the mobile device. Its distance from the satellite can be calculated by the transit time of the signal. Compare the distance from three satellites and you can calculate the actual location of the device to within about 16 metres. OK so far?

Antonia Yes.

Presenter So if the mobile provider or another service provider has a database of information detailing what the customer is interested in, perhaps this is a service the customer subscribes and inputs to, then we mash up that data with the location of the device and look at which retail outlets, hotels, restaurants, etc. the device owner may want to know about. The GPS locations of those can be shown on a map of the local area displayed on the device screen and the user can go to them if they wish.

Antonia That sounds great. Where do I sign up?

UNIT 3, EXERCISE 4

Elizabeth Talking Software is an SME-sized software development company. We have three areas of expertise. First, we have about five Business Process Consultants who can analyse what business processes exist in each Cleverbox and Smart Route department. This analysis is the start of the software development process and provides a specification or Software Requirements Analysis.

Secondly, if Cleverbox want us to develop this Software Requirements Analysis into some new, bespoke software for you, then we have approximately twenty software engineers, programmers, and coders in our Software Development team. These people take the Software Requirements Analysis and use it to design the software architecture and code and compile the software. All of their output is designed to be robust, modular, secure, and of course thoroughly tested for bugs. If you don't need a bespoke solution, then they could customize an existing software product to fit your needs.

Thirdly, we have a ten-strong Application Implementation team. Led by a Project Manager, they will work with Cleverbox to manage the successful implementation of any new software. They could install the bespoke software we have developed, they could install a customized product, or they could implement an off-the-shelf package too. As the rollout of software across a business is so complex, they design and work to a strict project plan to make sure that the cutover to the new software is a success and we won't sign off the project until everything is in a steady state.

UNIT 3, EXERCISE 12

12

Jane	Hello everybody and welcome to the ERP Rollout kickoff call. We've already signed the contract with Talking Software and have identified you as relevant stakeholders for this call. I'll pass over to Elizabeth to explain the project.
Elizabeth	Hi everyone. OK I'd like to explain the next nine months when we will be rolling out the ERP software across the Cleverbox business units. Sticking to these dates is a critical success factor as we do not want any slippage. First of all, Jane, I understand you own IT Infrastructure with the MPLS network required to be in by the 17th of Feb and the Datacentre ready by the 22nd at the latest. Any delay here will be a bottleneck for the entire programme. I hope that's OK.
Jane	That's fine.
Elizabeth	Great. Pedro will liaise with you all to ensure data and software templates for each department are completed on time and within spec. Pedro, would you mind explaining the workstreams involved?
Pedro	Sure. First of all, we need to identify all the data that you each have to migrate to the new system which I would like at the end of this month. Then each department will construct a data template in the software, this needs to be done before the end of next month. This will help to remove any dirty or unclean data from being input to the new system.

After that, the database will be configured to accept the template and data on the 15th of March. Finally, any customization of your templates or processes must be completed one week later.

Elizabeth	Thanks Pedro. Once this is complete we will start the cutover to the new software, department by department, starting with Finance. On the first Monday of each month we will put in place a data freeze on your old application. Approximately one week later we will begin the data migration which will take about five weeks per department. Then testing will begin. Testing and problem resolution will last about four weeks then that department will be cut over. Any questions?
Mustafa	It's Mustafa here. We have to migrate the data starting on the 8th of April. That would be general ledger and payroll for us. Can we include cash management and accounts payable?
Elizabeth	Yes, Mustafa, they are within scope so it's OK. That reminds me if anyone has anything that's out of scope then we can fast track a change control as long as we receive the request by the end of March.
Chuck	HR here. Will our data freeze from May 3rd mean we have to stop hiring people?
Elizabeth	No, Chuck, you can input new employee's data straight into the new templates.
Xu	Hi. It's Manufacturing. The testing between August 18th and September 24th when we cut over is a very important dependency for us. Can we extend the test period until September 30th?
Elizabeth	I'm sorry. I'm afraid we can't Xu. We can't afford any slippage at all.
Sandra	Elizabeth, it's Sandra. What about if we want to cut over early, before our deadline on August 23rd?
Elizabeth	Sandra, that's fine if you are happy that the testing is complete and you've signed it off.
Jane	No more questions? OK then. In terms of governance we will have a stakeholders' call like this once a month to make sure we deliver a successful handover on the 29th of October. Thanks for your time. Goodbye.

UNIT 4, EXERCISE 2

13

Dave	Hi Jerry. Africa now, is it? So where are you and how are we going to talk to you this time?
Jerry	Well I'm sharing a Sat phone right now with Mgumba, our local guy. We're in the Upper River region. We've been travelling around trying to figure out what telecoms infrastructure is available. What we have found out is that West Africa is connected to Europe via the South Atlantic 3 West Africa Submarine Cable which has a capacity of 120 gigabytes. The nearest cable landing point is over the border.

There are microwave radio links from there to here. The country is also connected internationally via satellite and Intelsat Earth Station 1. So there are redundant connections and services coming into the country. Some of the international data network providers are starting to look at expanding their networks here and putting some nodes in the capital and the other main city. So we may be able to get MPLS or global Ethernet services in the future.

Dave   So Mgumba, what's the in-country infrastructure like?

Mgumba   Historically, in-country, we have had poor fixed line infrastructure. A second national operator was licensed in May giving us some choice instead of just the PTT. The country's electricity utility is also laying fibre and leasing capacity to telecom operators. To its credit, the PTT is rolling out a national fibre backbone to serve the existing local telephone exchanges. In the mountainous regions they are erecting point to point microwave towers as it saves time and is much cheaper to implement. The telephone exchanges are mostly electro-mechanical but they are phasing these out and putting in exchanges with digital switching equipment. Copper fixed lines are being rolled out. So there's a lot going on at a national level but teledensity is still well below African average.

Dave   Jerry, what services can you get to the office? What about the local loop?

Jerry   Well, our office is about 250m from the local exchange. So we should definitely be able to get PSTN and depending on the switching equipment in the exchange and quality of the local loop, possibly DSL. All the local loops are copper twisted pair and the lead times are really long. There will not be fibre available to the customers' premises for at least two years. The problem with the copper pairs in the ground is that they get dug up and stolen so we will need to ask that our services are provided using telegraph poles and terminated straight into my second floor office window. It should support our voice and email requirements. The other option of course is to put a VSAT dish on the roof which would probably provide better reliability, but I think we need to apply for a licence via the landlord and that could be really expensive.

UNIT 4, EXERCISE 14

Greg   Hi. Is that Florence?

Florence   Yes it is.

Greg   Florence it's Greg from the NOC in London. I understand you've got a problem as I've got Trouble Ticket 2574 in front of me. Is it OK to talk now and on this number?

Florence   Yes it's fine. I've lost my voice and data connectivity to my desktop, that's why I'm using my mobile.

Greg   OK Florence. What I'm going to do is walk you through a series of tests to see if we can locate the problem. Is that OK?

Florence   Sure. Fire away.

Greg   OK. Can you just confirm that you have power at your desktop and within the office?

Florence   Yes, I've checked that. The PC is on and everyone else is OK so we have power.

Greg   OK. Next can you look at the back of your PC and check that the yellow Ethernet cable is plugged in to the port on your PC and following that check it is plugged into the RJ45 connector on the wall.

Florence   Hold on. ...Yes, they're both fine.

Greg   OK. Good. Now, after that, I have to check the LAN hub is functioning but as you said everyone else is OK, so that must mean the hub is functional.
So the next step Florence, is that I need to test the VPN network from my end, so hold on while I do this .... That's tested OK and I can see the router on my network management application so that's all working fine.

Florence   So Greg, if the WAN works and the LAN works, it looks like it's something to do with my PC?

Greg   You're right as my next step is to remotely check the network card on your PC. Let me try ... I can't, it's not responding. It's your network card. Florence, can you reboot your PC for me please.

Florence   OK. One second ... OK it's coming back now.

Greg   OK. Let me do that test again. Yes it's working. I can see you now and your IP address is 10.223.44.867. I'll just check that with a ping test. Yes that's successful.

Florence   Great. I can see that my email is coming in now and I've got connectivity.

Greg   OK, the last step is for me to just do a round trip delay test and confirm that the latency is acceptable. Hold on. Yes, its 75mS which is underneath the threshold. Florence, if it's OK with you, I'll close the ticket.

Florence   That's fine. Thanks so much Greg. Bye.

UNIT 5, EXERCISE 1

15 Good morning, and welcome, my name is Helmut. First I'll tell you a little about our data centre, then we'll have a tour inside the data centre and then back to this meeting room for a Q and A session.

So we are a Tier 4 data centre providing 99.995% availability for your mission critical data and applications. That's only 0.4 hours downtime per year. As you noticed on your way here this morning, we are deep in the Bavarian countryside away from any airports, flight paths, or terrorist targets, and on a raised plain to protect us from the potential of flooding. As you have just experienced, we have strict security procedures to get into the site and then further restrictions on moving around within the site such as fencing and barriers; we have 24-hour security guards and CCTV. Our own employees have to go through that security every day and they must use biometrics to move between the compartments in the data centre itself. There are no exceptions to all of this security.

In terms of power, we have two separate power feeds from the grid, coming in from the east and the west, along with our own UPS systems and generators on site. We also have boxes of candles for when the lights do go out. Ha Ha. Only joking. To ensure we have resilient communications connectivity, our telecoms services come into the north of the site and the south of the site from different network POPs and we use two different carriers to ensure full redundancy and separacy. This more or less guarantees that we do not suffer from network outages.

So your data will be protected from plane crashes, power cuts, network outages, bombs, and to a certain extent malicious employees. We have, of course, eliminated any single point of failure to protect ourselves and your data from those crazy guys in the diggers.

UNIT 5, EXERCISE 3

16 So we are now inside the central apparatus room. As you saw, I had to use my fingerprint on the scanner to get us in here, which I am authorized to do. Only certain employees are authorized to be within the data centre itself.

We have here 200,000 square feet of data centre and a capacity of 200 petabytes of data, that's the same as all the printed material in the world. As you can see we are standing on raised, perforated tiles. Underneath these are the telecom cable trays carrying all of the CAT6 and Ethernet cables. Also below us are the power cables that serve all the equipment. Above us in the ceilings we have our extraction and cooling systems to allow us to maintain the correct temperature and humidity specified by the equipment manufacturers. We have to ensure that this environment is maintained 24/7 and 365 days a year. We have designed the layout to have hot aisles

at the rear of the cabinets and cold aisles at the front of the cabinets. This helps to minimize hot spots. Also above us are the smoke detectors and clean agent fire suppression units, should a fire ever break out.

All the equipment, the servers, blades, etc. are housed in 19-inch racks which are mounted floor to ceiling. For all that data we have about 15,000 racks holding about 300,000 servers. You can see the front of the blades in the racks here. Any alarm conditions are indicated by the front panel LEDs but also in our management centre. Technicians can also use CDROM, disk, or USB ports to carry out any local maintenance or back-up tasks for individual servers. At the back here you can see all of the Ethernet ports that connect everything. These are the fans that pump out all this hot air. Here you can see the power supply for the racks and blades.

We of course provide all of the servers for your use but some clients do provide their own which we collocate and manage for them according to their own bespoke SLA. Most of the applications we host here for clients are ERP and CRM systems but there are all sorts of applications hosted here for all sorts of industries.

UNIT 5, EXERCISE 5

17

Rupert	Well, Helmut, that was a very impressive tour of your facility. But you know outsourcing our data to a third party is a very serious decision. There are a few things, like what would happen when you do go down for that 0.4 hours per annum? What happens if that is during our trading period?
Helmut	Well, we haven't had an outage since we have been here. We monitor everything here 24/7 at our management centre which you can see over there. But if there was a comms outage we would switch to the back-up service without you losing service. We have fully redundant services into the site so we'd use these. We would contact the PTT, who we have a very strict agreement with, to carry out fault finding and rectification. Our SLA with them is for a one-hour break fix. If we lost power, our own back-up power systems would start and we wouldn't lose power at all. If there were a problem with the cooling systems, our managers would see alarms about that before it affected the equipment. In the event of one of your servers going down, our managers would see alarms going off in the management centre and they would isolate and change out your equipment straight away. Your downtime would be a matter of minutes.
Rupert	OK, that all sounds fine. But worst case, you've got all our data, supposing there was an earthquake or you got hit by a plane, what would happen then?

Helmut   Well look, no system is infallible, we cannot protect against everything but perhaps I should explain, we have a complete mirror of this site in Switzerland. So all your data is backed up at that site. So if the worst came to the worst, at least there is a copy of all your data in another place. Should anything terrible occur, you would need to have standby communications links to our site in Switzerland and you would be OK. If that were to happen, you would switch over to the hot standby site and would continue to trade.

Rupert   Ah, great. At least knowing that, I would be able to sleep at night.

UNIT 5, EXERCISE 8

18

A   I'm what they call a white-hat hacker. I've worked for the bank for about five years. I was in the IT department responsible for the firewalls and encryption software. But I really like programming and when the bank had a few hackers starting to penetrate the network I got involved in keeping them out.

B   So, a white-hat hacker is a computer hacker, but when we expose security flaws we let the organization know they have a problem, rather than exploiting it. We fight against black-hat hackers – criminals who will exploit these problems.

C   For example I'll run a "ping sweep" on a bank's network to see who is connected and then do some TCP/IP fingerprinting to find out what operating system people are using. I may then run a sniffer which will watch out for their passwords as they key them in. Now, if they aren't using say 128bit SSL certificates, their data isn't encrypted and then I can access the bank's network and data centre and do what I like. I don't of course; I tell the bank I have found a weakness or a user who needs to improve their online security.

D   What would my advice be to people to remain secure online? Make sure you are using anti-virus software and you download any updates to keep out the latest viruses and worms. Use a personal firewall.

E   Never respond to emails that look like they are from the bank, you know, phishing. This type of activity is becoming ever more sophisticated, spear phishing is far more targeted, not just the blanket spam of a few years ago. These emails look like they really are meant for you as they are relevant to your business area. The email will contain something that looks like an attachment but actually it's a piece of malware like a Trojan or a worm. This software will sit on a computer and send the black-hat hacker personal information, passwords, credit card numbers, bank account details. These then allow them to hack into the bank's data centre and steal thousands of people's account numbers and sell them to other gangs.

UNIT 6, EXERCISE 9

Chen   OK everyone, we need to decide which managed service offering we need to support our technology and what our Service Level Agreement should be. That's SLA, right Betty?

Betty   Right, SLA. Anurak could you explain the options for us?

Anurak   OK. Since we looked at the adverts I have spoken to ThaiManagement to understand some details about each of the propositions. The Bronze Service offers us a maintenance response time of the next working day and the helpdesk is available 9 to 5 Monday to Friday.

Betty   Anurak that's not good enough for us. It's vital that we have cover seven days a week.

Anurak   Yes, I agree. And the same goes for the helpdesk, because we're very busy Saturdays and Sundays with people hiring cars at the weekend. We need at least the Silver Service with the helpdesk available seven days a week. But I think we actually need the four-hour response, 24/7 helpdesk availability like the Gold Service.

Betty   Looking at this, it's the same for fault monitoring. It's important that we have it 24/7 like the Gold Service, but we don't need a dedicated team to do that. So really we want to have the cheaper shared team for proactive fault monitoring as long as it's 24/7.

Anurak   OK, good idea. In terms of performance monitoring, we could go for network-only monitoring with the Silver Service or network and applications monitoring with the Gold Service. Any views?

Betty   Let's just have performance monitoring for the network because that really is important. Our applications are pretty simple; I don't think we need it for them.

Chen   OK, let's look at the commercial aspects. Reporting, what's important to us?

Anurak   Well, I don't think we can wait for a month to receive reports. If we have user or customer service problems because of our technology then we need to be able to see what's going on there and then.

Betty   I agree. I think it's very important that we can have real time reporting like the Gold Service offers.

Chen   OK, what about a Service Manager? Can we share one or is it essential to have the Gold

	Service which includes a dedicated Service Manager?
Anurak	I think we can go for a shared Service Manager in the Silver Service. This will keep our costs down. We don't have that many sites to manage. As long as there's someone who's familiar with our infrastructure, then I think a shared one would be fine.
Chen	OK, fine with me. As far as the asset buyback is concerned, I'd really like the cheque on day one, what a great offer!
Anurak	But boss, that means we'd lose control of our IT. I know you'd like the money up front at the start of the contract but in my opinion it's not as important as retaining control over our technology and keeping it up to date.
Chen	But they are also offering a technology refresh to upgrade the technology on an annual basis. What about that?
Betty	Do we really need that – surely we're in the best position to know what needs replacing?
Anurak	And we'd lose control…
Chen	Well, I'll think about it but it looks as if we want some of the Silver Service and some of the Gold Service. As far as the cost goes, the Silver is 16,500 a month … we can manage that no problem, but the Gold is more than double … Anyway, I'll see what I can do … it looks like I've got a negotiation on my hands.

UNIT 6, EXERCISE 10

🔊 20

Chen	Thanks for coming in to see me. I've discussed your offers with my team and I'd like to talk you through what we are after.
Maliwan	Have you had a chance to look through the different options?
Chen	Yes, we've had a good look.
Maliwan	Great, so which of the three do you think would suit you best?
Chen	Well, based on our business requirements the SLA we are looking for is a mixture of both the Silver and the Gold Service. Would you consider a compromise between the two?
Maliwan	Well, why don't you tell me what you are after and I'll see what we can do.
Chen	For maintenance cover we require a four-hour response and 24/7 helpdesk as we have people arriving from the airport at all hours and if we have a fault, an eight-hour response is just too long for us.
Maliwan	OK that's not a problem, that's all covered by the Gold Service.
Chen	Yes, but for fault monitoring we only need a shared team, not a dedicated team.
Maliwan	We can manage that.

Chen	The only thing is that we do need the shared team 24/7, not just during business hours.
Maliwan	I see … well…, no that's OK, we can do that at a reasonable price, but only if you also have a shared Service Manager.
Chen	OK, I can accept that. Thank you. That's fine as we don't have that many sites and for performance monitoring we only want the network covered.
Maliwan	Yes, of course.
Chen	For reporting we require the Gold offering of real time online. How do you suggest we deal with that?
Maliwan	I'll have to think about that. Keep going.
Chen	Well that leaves the asset buyback and technology refresh which, to be honest, we were undecided on.
Maliwan	Well I won't be able to split them. You have to have both or neither.
Chen	OK, I don't have a problem with that.
Maliwan	Well if you take the asset buyback and the technology refresh of the Gold Service, then I could contribute the real time reporting to the deal. How does that sound?
Chen	OK, but we can't afford to pay 35,000 Baht per month per user. What can you do about that?
Maliwan	OK let me summarize first. You are taking the cheaper Silver Service elements for fault monitoring, performance monitoring and the shared Service Manager. And Gold Service for all other parts of the SLA. How would you feel about 33,000 per month per user?
Chen	Go to 27,000 and we have a deal.
Maliwan	OK, let's compromise, I'll meet you in the middle at 30,000.
Chen	OK. Let's shake on that. It's a deal.

UNIT 7, EXERCISE 11

🔊 21

Lara	OK, what are you here to pitch today?
Anna	We want to develop lamppost.com, a social networking site for dogs and their owners. We need to raise $750,000 seed funding to get us going.
Lara	Err, OK. Keep going
Paul	There are 72 million pet dogs in the US and therefore about the same number of owners. We have built a prototype that allows owners to input their street name. Lamppost.com presents a local map showing where nearby dogs and owners live. The owners can click on the dog they think their dog will get on with and they can go for a walk together. There's also a local blog and messageboard on the site where owners can arrange group walks or if they are working, can ask for people to take their dogs for a walk during the day.

Alan	OK guys, how are you going to monetize this?
Anna	Users register on the site for $1 per year. This creates an account for them. We will have an ecommerce section where owners can buy collars, leads, food, etc. Vets' Surgeries will also advertise on the site using banners, which will be another revenue stream for us. We project two million registered users year one, five million registered users year two and fifteen million registered users by year three. When users register they have to provide an email address, so of course we can use these to form a mailing list that has a value.
Alan	And technically, where are you with this?
Paul	We have bought the domain name lamppost.com. We have built a prototype that we are hosting on our own servers at the moment. We've spoken to a third party hosting company who can provide dedicated servers, internet connectivity, data backup, and archiving for a monthly fee.
Lara	OK guys, thanks; we'll have a think about it.

UNIT 7, EXERCISE 14

Alan	OK guys, start your presentation.
Yuniko	Thank you. We are video game developers and require funding to develop BIGFIGHT which will be a new, globally-networked war game. We are looking for start up funding of $2m. The game will be designed for all three of the main consoles on the market that have a broadband or WiFi connection.
Tomas	But more importantly we will also be developing an on-demand networked version for PCs that have good enough sound cards and graphics cards or even TVs that have Internet connectivity.
Yuniko	The game will be streamed across the 1.5 billion Internet connections around the world into users' homes. This enables citizens to join in a giant battle representing their home countries, which we can identify from their IP address.
Tomas	Gamers can join their country's army and be represented in the game as a soldier. They can control what the soldier does using their keyboard and controllers or joysticks.
Luke	OK. What do you need the money for? And what revenue streams do you anticipate?
Yuniko	Well we have put together a team of game designers and opensource video game developers. We think development will take about a year and then six months of trialling and testing. So we need the money to support that development activity. In terms of revenues, online customers will pay a $10

sign up fee, then a $4 monthly subscription. Or people can purchase the software in a store for $39.99

UNIT 7, EXERCISE 18

Stuart	OK, so here's the mock-up of the screen so you can see the layout and get the look and feel of the site.
Paul	OK, cool.
Stuart	So top left we have your logo. To the right of that, so the top centre and top right of the screen, we expect that space to be banners sponsored by companies that want to advertise on the site.
Paul	Great, yes, advertising revenue is important to us.
Stuart	Below that, going across the screen, we have a row of tabs that let you navigate the site. So I think the tabs will be Homepage then Social Networking then Blog then Products and finally News. Is that order OK?
Paul	Actually I think we want the Blog to be last, so on the right. Also we want a tab for a resources page so that people can download pdfs on products or dog health issues or whatever.
Stuart	OK, no problem. So on the homepage tab we have a block of text explaining the service. In the middle column we've got a couple of JPEGs of happy looking dogs and on the right of that, we have the sign up and sign in buttons. But basically a very clear and simple design … When someone clicks to *Sign Up*, they go through to a webform that they fill in with their details to sign up to the service. Obviously we will create an ecommerce facility so they can securely put in their credit card details for their annual fee.
Paul	Great.
Stuart	When they click on *Sign In*, then they are prompted to put in their username and password.
Paul	And if they forget their password?
Stuart	They click on this button below: *Forgot your password* and we send a reminder email to the email address on the database. Once they are in, they can go to the Social Networking page and upload images of their dog or themselves, preferably as JPEGs but we could accept GIFs, and set their profile details so other users can see them. Once they have done that, they are live. If they see a dog owner or a dog that they like, they can click on the image and get a pop-up that gives further information. Or vice versa their details will pop up if they are clicked on.

UNIT 8, EXERCISE 1

Presenter Good morning and welcome to our radio show looking at Telecoms and IT and its impact on society. Today we are looking at emerging digital technology in Healthcare. We're going to predict how digital technology might affect one patient's pathway of care in the near future. Let's imagine the case of Sue who has a suspected heart attack. We have with us Lynn, a paramedic, Malik, an A & E doctor, a hospital manager, Imogen, and Helen, a cardiac nurse.

UNIT 8, EXERCISE 2

Presenter So let's start with Lynn, you're a paramedic … so what will happen when Sue starts to have chest pains at home?

Lynn Well, when Sue falls ill she dials the emergency services, speaks to the operator and asks for an ambulance. We will be there in less than ten minutes as we all have GPS location equipment to work out which ambulance is nearest to the patient and then we are directed to the patient automatically by the Sat Nav using the most direct route. We rush her to the hospital, monitoring her all the way.

Presenter And Malik, you are a doctor at A & E Admissions

Malik Yes, I am. We will already have Sue's full patient records by the time she is brought in to hospital. The ambulance will radio her Health Number ahead, and with that, all her details can be downloaded from the National Patient Records Database and I will receive all the information here on my Mobile Clinical Assistant over the wireless LAN. This allows me to access all information whilst being as close as possible to the patient.

Presenter Imogen, as the Hospital IT Manager, it sounds as if the hospital will be brimming with technology.

Imogen Well, the hospital will be connected to a national data network and huge national database holding terabytes of every civilian's medical records. The whole hospital will be wireless-enabled so that with the correct security, actually a swipe card and password, doctors or nurses will be able to access a patient's records wherever they are in the hospital. They will be able to use their data tablet to set up a VoIP call with the patient's GP to discuss anything they're not sure of before treating the patient. They will be able to do a 3D CT scan and transmit the huge image file to a remote specialist, say in London, and, using our screen sharing application, will be able to get a second opinion within moments. All the hospitals will use the Digital Imaging and Communications in Medicine (DICOM) standard for handling, storing, printing, and transmitting information in medical imaging which allows us to send anything over any TCP/IP network, anywhere in the world to get images in front of the right medical expert.

Presenter So Helen, once the panic is over and Sue's condition is understood what will happen to her?

Helen I am a cardiac nurse, and I would look after Sue when we receive her as an inpatient for observation. I would visit her every day, and log on to the hospital systems using my digital clipboard. The clipboard would recognize the RFID tag in Sue's wristband. This tagging is a safeguard to make sure we don't give the wrong drugs to the wrong patients. I could give her tablets and the barcode reader on my clipboard would recognize and record the drugs I was giving her. If I went to use the wrong drug, the barcode reader would give an alert to prevent me doing this. I'd also take a few measurements, input them into the clipboard which would then transmit this information into Sue's digital patient records, so they are always up to date.

Presenter And how about Sue's care once she's back at home?

Helen Sue would still be monitored remotely at home. She would put on a monitoring device every morning that measures her temperature, blood pressure, respiration, and heart rate. She would then plug it into a broadband adaptor and the data would be transmitted to a database in the hospital and added to her patient records. The application would automatically display the data in a graph for the doctors to look at. The software would also be programmed to send an email alert to Sue's GP Surgery to arrange an appointment if her readings go over any thresholds or if the software calculates she is running out of medication, it automatically places an order for more which will arrive recorded delivery before she runs out.

OXFORD
UNIVERSITY PRESS

Great Clarendon Street, Oxford OX2 6DP

Oxford University Press is a department of the University of Oxford.
It furthers the University's objective of excellence in research, scholarship,
and education by publishing worldwide in

Oxford New York

Auckland Cape Town Dar es Salaam Hong Kong Karachi
Kuala Lumpur Madrid Melbourne Mexico City Nairobi
New Delhi Shanghai Taipei Toronto

With offices in

Argentina Austria Brazil Chile Czech Republic France Greece
Guatemala Hungary Italy Japan Poland Portugal Singapore
South Korea Switzerland Thailand Turkey Ukraine Vietnam

OXFORD and OXFORD ENGLISH are registered trade marks of
Oxford University Press in the UK and in certain other countries

© Oxford University Press 2009

The moral rights of the author have been asserted

Database right Oxford University Press (maker)

First published 2009

2013 2012 2011 2010 2009
10 9 8 7 6 5 4 3 2 1

Any websites referred to in this publication are in the public domain
and their addresses are provided by Oxford University Press for
information only. Oxford University Press disclaims any responsibility
for the content

ISBN: 978 0 19 456959 0

Printed in China

ACKNOWLEDGEMENTS

Prepared for OUP by: Starfish Design Editorial and Project Management
Ltd.

*The authors and publisher are grateful to those who have given permission to
reproduce the following extracts and adaptations of copyright material:*
p20 From 'Contactless payment: Touchy Subject' by Joanna Perry, 18
September 2008, from *Retail Week* www.retail-week.com. Reproduced
by kind permission; p55 From '5 Can't-Miss Vendor Negotiation Tips'
by Martin Ewing, Pactoris, CIO, 18 February 2009, from www.cio.com.
Reproduced by kind permission.

*The publisher would like to thank the following for their kind permission to
reproduce photographs and other copyright material*: istock pp4 (Phone/
Anna Khomulo & Kathy Konkle), 6 (Businessman/Pesky Monkey),
(Businesswoman/Tyler Stalman), (Businessman/Ravi Tahilramani),
Fotolia p15 (Computer customer/Andres R), istock p15 (Touchscreen
phone/Baris Simsek), (Laptop/Luca di Filippo), Shutterstock p18
(Barcode scanner/Loannis Loannou), istock p18 (Touchscreen phone/
Juliya Shumskaya), 31 (Submarine cable/Janne Ahvo), (Satellite/Andrey
Volodin), (Global ethernet/Kiyoshi Takahase Segundo), (US network/
Mark Stay), (Digital switching loop/Suprijono Suharjoto), (Fibreoptic
laying/Nancy Louie), 33 (Twisted pairs/Georgios Alexandris), 39 (Third
world streets/Online creative media), (Development/Alex Jeffries),
(Business park/James C. Pruitt), (Irish countryside/Rolf Weschke), 40
(Front of blade rack/Katharina Wittfeld), (Back of blade rack/Carolina
K. Smith, M.D.), 42 (Data center/Amy Walters), 48 (Real estate/Brent
Holland), (Boutique/Cebas), Shuttterstock p48 (Couple/Ronen),
(Receiving dish/Dejan Gileski), istock p56 (Billboard/Sang Nguyen), (TV/
Gabriel Moisa), (Direct mail/Shawn Gearhart), 61 (Interview/Marcin
Balcerzak), 67 (Nurse/Dean Scott), 69 (Eye/Andrew Figgins), (Camera/
Sharon Dominick), (Screens/David H. Lewis), (Satellite/Pete Stopher), 75
(Phone/Marilyn Nieves), (MP3 player/Largeformat4x5), (RJ45 connector/
Godfried Edelman), 77 (Laptop/CostinT), (Portable speakers/Ronen),
(Router/Sam Brogio)

Cover images courtesy of: Corbis (main image/Ed Kashi), (top left/Paul
Edmondson), Getty Images (bottom left/Seth Joel/Riser).

Illustrations by: I-Creo Design

*The authors and publishers would like to thank the following for their help in
developing the book*: Ray ffrench of Suila Ltd., Hazel Britton, an English
lecturer at Aalen University

 MultiROM

English for Telecoms is accompanied by a MultiROM which
has a number of features.

Interactive exercises to practise useful phrases, vocabulary,
and communication through your computer.

Listening extracts. These are in enhanced audio format that
can be played on a conventional CD-player or through the
audio player on your computer.

If you have any problems, please check the technical
support section of the readme file on the MultiROM.